The Wehrmacht series by Horst Weitzer translated by
George Hirst available from New English Library:

PANZERGRENADIER
GENOCIDE AT ST-HONOR

PANZERGRENADIER

Horst Weitzer

translated by George Hirst

NEW ENGLISH LIBRARY

A New English Library Original Publication, 1981

First NEL Paperback Edition November 1981

NEL Books are published by
New English Library,
Barnard's Inn, Holborn,
London EC1N 2JR, a division of Hodder and Stoughton Ltd.

Printed and bound in Great Britain by
©ollins, Glasgow

0 450 05249 4

Chapter One

A sudden, deafening, crack of thunder overhead coincided with the first ranging shots of the American artillery barrage. Obersturmfuhrer Franz Sprenger, commanding the Waffen SS 3rd Panzergrenadier Company, was the first casualty. He had been perched on the edge of a foxhole dug amongst the roots of a high bocage hedge, scowling through binoculars at the US 5th Armoured Division positions a kilometre to the west when the first HE shell burst a dozen metres to his right. A sliver of flying shrapnel nipped out both his eyes and the bridge of his nose, on its way to a shattered tree stump where it embedded itself deep into the bark. Sprenger threw himself flat on to his back, screaming, his hands clasped over the bloody sockets whilst the Company Headquarters Section stared in disbelief at what had happened to their commander.

As further shells pinpointed their positions, so heavy spots of rain began to ping off their steel helmets. More thunder! More rain! More ranging shots! — much farther back this time, accurately bracketing the panzergrenadiers. Now, nobody had time to worry about Obersturmfuhrer Franz Sprenger. They guessed that those lucky first ranging shots would have been observed by American forward gunnery officers, who would waste no time in giving their heavy and medium batteries the order to fire for effect.

Within seconds, the ground around the hedge and the strip of woodland to the rear would begin to pitch and heave under a torrent of high-explosive and scything metal. Sprenger would lie there, blind and screaming, for soon his cries would be lost amongst the thunder of the barrage.

There was no protection in this bloody wood. None at all. The trees were already shredded and the earth around them was sand and roots, which would cascade with every shellburst, leaving the bodies of the panzergrenadiers exposed to the shrieking shrapnel.

Now the rain was coming down in a solid wall of water, bouncing centimetres high from the sun-baked farm vehicle tracks alongside the bocage hedge, where it broke into an opaque mist which obscured the American positions a kilometre to the west as efficiently as a smokescreen.

More shells burst within the bracketed area. Agonised screams erupted from mortally wounded men somewhere at the rear, where a conscript replacement suddenly bolted from his foxhole, zig-zagging through the shellbursts, insane with fear. An officer from the 2nd Company shot him down with his MP-40 Schmeiser maschinenpistole, leaving him writhing in the pouring rain, the mud and the shrapnel.

'Watch your fronts, goddammit!'

SS Sturmann Klaus Stumm, NCO commanding the 7·92mm MG-42 Spandau machine gun section of the 2nd Platoon, yelled at his team at the top of his voice, viciously swinging a loaded ammunition belt at SS-mann Helmut Kleiser, who had turned at the unexpected drumming of the officer's Schmeiser. The last few rounds crashed hard against the rim of Kleiser's steel helmet and the metal link-piece sliced a strip of flesh from his jaw. He spun round with murder in his eyes, grabbing at the belt, but Stumm wrenched it free. Kleiser was on the point of making a second grab, but when he caught sight of Stumm's crazed eyes he changed his mind. Nobody but a madman would risk mixing it with Stumm during a battle. Even a farm boy like Kleiser knew that his end could be slower and infinitely more terrible than that of the recruit who had just panicked under his first barrage. But, all the same, he held Stumm's blood-streaked, pale-blue eyes, set in a face made gaunt by months of battle, hunger and remorseless killing; the thick blond stubble of a week's beard spreading under the tight chin-strap of the steel helmet.

Anyway, Kleiser excused himself hanging on to his self-esteem, the sturmann was right! Any minute now the barrage would cease and American Sherman tanks with their 17-pounder tank-busting Firefly guns would come blasting through the rain. In support would be infantry, storming their positions in the wood, outnumbering the panzergrenadiers four or five to one. Every man needed to face his front!

SS-mann Franz Kreutzmann, No 1 on the MG-42 Spandau, already had the first length of belt threaded into the breech and Stumm was meticulously checking the gun's width of traverse on its tripod, his sudden flare-up with Kleiser already wiped from his mind.

But Kleiser continued to watch the NCO, his eyes dropping to the dark band of material on his right sleeve which contrasted with the rest of the sun-bleached uniform. For that was where Sturmann Klaus Stumm had worn the black, silver-threaded cuff title of the infamous SS Grossdeutschland Division. Though severely wounded, both Stumm and Kreutzmann had miraculously made it back home, with remnants of the shattered 4th Panzer Army, from the battles of the Russian Dnieper in January 1944. Both men had claimed that if they could survive the Dnieper, then they'd have nothing to worry about in Normandy from a rabble of green Yanks — but that had been three months ago at the time of Omaha Beach and things had changed dramatically since then!

The American shelling increased to reach a new crescendo and forked lightning from deep in the thunder clouds spat down at them with the viciousness of a cobra, worrying the crews of the Panzer VI Tigers a kilometre to the rear and intensely vulnerable in their steel boxes with long, waving, radio antennae.

Heavy machine gun fire from a score of directions began to enfilade the panzergrenadier positions. This was ball-spliced with tracer which raked their foxholes like horizontal brass rods, gouging lumps from the trees, cutting furrows into the soft earth, seeking out the unprotected bodies of the soldiers crouching there. Screams issued from the rear, more panic, more ragged Schmeiser fire.

Rain! Lightning! Thunder! The blast of high-explosive and scything metal! Then, from farther to the west they heard a sudden concerted roar of tank engines. This was the main threat which the panzergrenadiers had been expecting; but along with the cacophony there also came the promise of positive action and a chance to hit back.

In the forward positions, grenadiers crouching behind infantry anti-tank weapons eased the hollow-charge grenades into the cradles and wiped away mud and water from the ring and bead sights.

'Stand-by!'

This was Untersturmfuhrer Dieter Brever, who had assumed command of the 3rd Company with Sprenger gone.

And, as the roar of his command tailed off amongst the mist and the dripping trees, the American barrage ceased as though it had been turned off at a master switch.

Again: 'Stand-by!'

As he shouted, he simultaneously fired a Kampfpistole from which a red signal flare soared high above the trees. Immediately, down came the Wehrmacht counter-barrage, pre-ranged on to the American forward positions, from

7

medium artillery and Panther self-propelled gun batteries two kilometres to the east. And, as the first assault wave of attacking American armour nosed upwards from hull-down start-line positions into the flat terrain of no-man's-land between the opposing armies, a curtain of high-calibre shells patterned the ground ahead of them. The Shermans bucked on their tracks and, through the rain and the curling cordite fumes, the waiting panzergrenadiers watched full lengths of track snake high into the air from their racing sprocket wheels.

Sturmann Klaus Stumm and his MG-42 Section crouched low over the Spandau; Kreutzmann holding level the ammunition belt which would soon jerk and writhe through the breech. At the other side of the machine gun, Kleiser was waiting to ease the empty belt clear, prepared to take over the firing position should Stumm be hit. A couple of metres away lay young Rudi Scherfe, not yet eighteen years old, his G-41 Mauser self-loading rifle at his shoulders, an MP-40 Schmeiser maschinenpistole at his elbow, there to gun down any close-range attacks by American infantrymen who had been lucky enough to escape the cones of Stumm's flailing bullets.

On either side of the machine gun, panzergrenadiers had moved forward with panzerschreck anti-tank weapons, fingers tight about the triggers, restless for a glimpse of the first American Sherman which sooner or later would burst through the screen of the counter-barrage. Farther to the left where the wood thickened into straggling brambles and bocage hedge, a team of four grenadiers were manning a 7·5cm PAK-41 anti-tank gun and already engaging the dull, zig-zagging shapes shrouded in mist. This was a crew doing a job without haste or panic, systematically adjusting to a decreasing range, loading and firing heedless of the flurry of American small-arms fire which whipped and snapped through the trees around them.

Forward American Shermans began shooting blindly into the woods, hoping for random casualties from both their seventeen-pounders and Browning heavy machine guns. But amongst the mist clearing under the blast of explosions, others could already be seen pulling out of the action with their turrets slewed round at a hundred and eighty degrees to the German positions, guns still firing. A half-hearted cheer erupted at the sight from the panzergrenadiers lining the edge of the wood, but as the Shermans thinned, they spotted the khaki uniforms and close-fitting 'flower-pot' helmets of American infantry for the first time. Immediately, an agitated splatter of small-arms fire rang out from the hedge.

The unterscharfuhrer commanding the section yelled above the din.

'Hold it, for Christ's sake! Hold it!'

There wasn't the ammunition to waste on shadowy figures, half-crouched and flitting amongst the flying shrapnel of the counter-barrage. If the gunners didn't stop them, then No 3 Company would hold their fire until they could read the names on the Americans' dog-tags!

As a result, the small-arms fire spluttered into nothing and at the same time the Wehrmacht forward artillery observation officer, positioned with the PAK-41 crew in the copse, called off the counter-barrage.

Immediately, a silence hung over the battlefield — as threatening as the blast of high-explosive and the staccato crackle of machine gun fire. Slowly, blue cordite fumes began to rise from the shallow shell craters and, with clearing vision, the panzergrenadiers began to pick out the line at which the first tentative American probe-attack had wilted and turned.

Within the arc of fire of Stumm's MG-42, three Shermans were smouldering, black smoke weaving and curling from their shattered turrets and engine housings. One of them exploded with a sudden belch of orange flame and the corpse of the tank commander, which had been hanging over the lip of his turret, was blown high into the trees, disintegrating in mid-air and showering blood and particles of flesh on to the bodies of wounded American infantrymen, who had attempted to claw themselves into the earth rather than take the risk of crawling back to their own lines.

The explosion caused movement in other marooned American tanks and on one of these the driver's hatch was flung back and the helmeted head of the driver appeared. From his antics it was evident that he was kicking with his feet, vainly trying to find sufficient leverage to thrust himself out of the compartment.

Stumm, who was watching, tossed a clod of earth at Rudi Scherfe which bounced off the top of his steel helmet, but Scherfe didn't even look in Stumm's direction. He already had an eye aligned to his rifle sights. First, pressure: a gentle, confident squeeze. The crack of the single shot. And with it the American tank man hurtled from the hatch under the momentum of the bullet which pierced his chest.

Scherfe still did not turn, his eyes roaming over the burning hulls of the blitzed Shermans. So they'd survived the first American onslaught! But what did that mean? The panzergrenadier companies deeper in the wood had suffered as many casualties as the Americans; their cries all the more shrill now that the heavy shelling had ceased. The Yanks would be back — maybe within minutes . . . General George Smith Patton and his 3rd American Army were too flushed with the success of their wild dash from the Normandy beachheads to be put off by the ineffective blooding of unseasoned troops. So far, they'd done no more than put out a probing thrust, testing the strength of the panzergrenadiers. Next time they'd come surging in with all they'd got.

The panzergrenadiers stood by their weapons. Silent. Eyes blurred with fatigue endlessly searching the distant American lines. Then, the immediate threat of a new bombardment as the air was shattered by the instantly recognisable whoosh-whoosh of heavy calibre shells, accompanied by 'pepper-pots' of mortar and small-arms fire.

The first salvo burst raggedly along the length of the bocage hedge.

Smoke!

Thick, curling, grey smoke which looked as solid as a stone wall began to seep into the defenders' eyes, at the same time tearing at their throats and causing them to vomit where they stood. And the rain, which still torrented down upon them, pressed the smoke close to the earth so that it rolled into their slit-trenches like a thick, mobile, carpet. Now the panzergrenadiers could barely open their eyes, dabbing at them with the backs of dirt-ingrained hands. Sensing an imminent all-out infantry attack, the gunnery forward observation officer again brought down the Wehrmacht counter-barrage and, as the first salvo exploded midway across the kilometre of no-man's-land, so the panzergrenadiers clutched their weapons and hung on.

Stumm wiped his running eyes and stared hard at his friend, Kreutzmann, noticing the man's hands which held the ammunition belt to the breech of the MG-42 machine gun. These were thin, emaciated hands, the fingers calloused with the dirt of months, the nails broken for want of vitamins, a festering sore bubbling green pus along the full length of the right hand. Kreutzmann sensed the sturmann's eyes on him and looked back at him, blinking away the pain, shaking his head. This wasn't Voronezh in winter when a man would die unless he could find shelter for the night. This was Voronezh in summer, which was worse because that had been the time when the Russians were fully mobile. In summer, Russian

10

armoured reconnaissance battalions, and even Cossack horse regiments, could turn the tide of a battle by moving from flank to flank in a chain of attacks which amounted to pincer movements, and could clip the life and strength from a beleaguered division – even a crack one like the Grossdeutschland!

Gott! If the Ruskies could do that kind of thing to the Grossdeutschland, then what would the Americans, with their endless supplies of weapons and ammunition, do to the schoolboy conscripts who made up most of the 3rd Panzergrenadier Company?

During the next half hour American smoke shells came down intermittently, thickening up the areas in which the light breeze and the rain had thinned, causing the panzergrenadiers to remain on stand-to, not knowing whether an American armoured thrust was imminent. But some of the soldiers, their limbs cramped into a crippling numbness, began to move warily about their positions in the swirling smoke, seeking some respite from the waterlogged foxholes and the black phlegm which the smoke had caused them to cough up from their tortured lungs.

Anticipating this, the Americans fired random machine gun bursts on fixed-lines, inevitably scoring hits without the gunners even glimpsing their targets. Grenadiers lay writhing in the open, their blood running freely into the oozing mud, many of them screaming for stretcher-bearers who didn't want to hear.

Then, as suddenly as before, the Americans ceased firing and once more that threatening silence hung over the German positions. It was a silence during which men stood upright in their foxholes, turning apprehensively from one position to the next, nerves taut, faces mirroring the hunger, privation and the accumulated battle-fatigue of their desperate withdrawal from the coast of Normandy to this insignificant spot on the map somewhere east of Laval. But they said little, the quickfire obscenities of the early weeks had long since given way to a turgid introspection which nagged at their consciousness, to be reborn in hideous nightmares during what brief sleep periods they were able to snatch.

From above came the sound of aircraft engines – scores of them – and, as one, the panzergrenadiers turned their faces to the clouds in the vain hope that these might be the Luftwaffe, long-promised by their officers to slow the momentum of the US 3rd Army advance. But there was nothing to be seen for, whatever aircraft were up there, they were well above the cloud-coverage. The watching men guessed that these must be US B-29 Flying Fortresses, for the Luftwaffe would have come in low at strafing height, regardless of the weather — Focke Wulf Fw-190s and Messerschmitt Bf-109s — fighter-bombers pinpointing American infantry, armour concentrations and artillery batteries.

The panzergrenadiers saw the first stick of bombs break through the clouds and come slanting earthwards. At first it appeared they would miss their positions by kilometres, but as they neared the ground so the angle narrowed and the soldiers crouched lower in their slit-trenches. And, as the first stick of bombs ploughed into the earth, a fireball raced a hundred metres into the wood, shrivelling up all that lay in its path.

Napalm!

Napalm, which could burn a man's lungs from his chest. The panzergrenadiers pressed themselves deeper into their foxholes, covering their faces with the mud and water which sloshed about their feet. There was no answer to napalm. No man could move. More bombs landed and the sea of flame which seared over them came like the sudden opening of a furnace door, singeing their hair and uniforms, causing the ammunition to explode in the bandoliers which they wore about their bodies.

The napalm bombardment lasted half an hour, the Americans taking their time and leaving long intervals during which nothing happened at all, causing the panzergrenadiers to frenziedly set up their weapons against the real possibility of a tank and infantry thrust. Then came more napalm and more casualties. Men were shrivelled to skeletons in the few seconds it took them to turn and dive for cover. And, ironically, with their burning there hung over the battlefield an appetising smell of roast flesh which contrasted with the sickly-sweet stench of death which had permeated their clothing for so long.

Then, after one prolonged bombing run and with the engines of the B-29s still drumming in the sky above them, there came the sudden roar and clash of tanks.

'Stand-to! Stand-to!'

This from Hauptscharfuhrer Hans Lind with hands cupped about his mouth, standing high in his foxhole, yelling at the top of his voice. The grenadiers sprang to their weapons. And at the first sight of an American Sherman nosing through the undergrowth, a grenadier at the corner of the copse pulled the trigger of his panzerschreck. But the hollow-charge grenade, heated by napalm, exploded in its cradle and the man disintegrated, leaving little more than a red purée which hung in glutinous strands from the surrounding bushes.

More smoke, which dropped neatly in mortar canisters along the line of the hedge.

The noise of the tank engines became louder as the armour moved in blocks into their smokescreen, their heavy guns shooting at random over open sights into the German positions, whilst the panzergrenadiers with one-shot panzerfaust weapons returned fire, aiming where the noise was most concentrated. There was a sudden lucky hit and a Sherman exploded not more than twenty metres from the German positions, the roar of its flame thinning the smoke around it.

Those in the forward positions breathed sighs of relief, eyes glued to the sights of their automatic weapons, leaving the tanks to the panzerfausts, the panzerschrecks and the few 7·5cm PAK-41s which were still functioning. Even if the spearhead of the American armour *did* manage to burst through the outer defensive screen, they'd get a hell of a surprise when they ran into the hull-down Panthers and Tigers primed to blast them off the face of the earth.

'Now!'

Sturmann Stumm didn't heed Kreutzmann's sharp cry for he'd already spotted the hazy outlines of American infantry, crouching behind their labouring tanks. But he didn't fire. There was still time! The smoke was thinning and the Shermans had edged too close to their positions for them to risk high-explosive. Stumm's teeth bared at the inevitable culmination of the battle. In the end it usually came to this. If a man stuck to his foxhole long enough, there'd always come a time when infantryman confronted infantryman.

There was no other formula. They'd let the armour through. The American infantry was something they could handle!

As the Wehrmacht counter-barrage crept closer towards the main American positions, he took his eyes from the sights of the MG-42 machine gun, glancing at Kreutzmann.

The old drill would still work!

Let the armour through and then seal off the supporting infantry from their own lines by dropping a barrage behind them. No escape! No reinforcements! The bastards would have to fight and when they got amongst each other they could forget about Schmeisers, Brownings and Thompsons. That would be a time for bayonets, knives and entrenching tools. Stumm's grin did no more than move the fair stubble on his chin, but Kreutzmann acknowledged it with a long look through his narrowed eyes. No way was this green American infantry likely to be a match for the 3rd Panzergrenadier Company. No match at all! This was going to be a bloody massacre!

The number of American infantry amongst the advancing Shermans was thickening; those at the rear being stampeded forward by the accuracy of the German barrage. The old drill! How many times had the Grossdeutschland Division worked it? How many senior Russian commanders had fallen for it? How many swaggering, newly-equipped Russian regiments had been annihilated? Now it was the Yanks' turn! No quarter! No prisoners! A grenadier couldn't see his mates shrivelled by napalm and, ten minutes later, feel charitable.

A Sherman suddenly loomed ahead with smoke swirling about its tracks and bogies like a white fluid. It had its hatches already battened down for battle – a crazy thing to do so close to enemy infantry, limiting visibility to the narrow oblongs of the periscopes. Green Yanks! A panzergrenadier bounded from his foxhole, clutching a sticky grenade which he rammed hard against the turret swivel-mounting as though he'd all the time in the world. His mates, still in the slit-trenches, sprayed the supporting infantry with 9mm Schmeiser bullets. Seconds later, with little more than a heavy thud, the sticky grenade exploded. As the plume of black smoke cleared it revealed that the turret of the Sherman had slipped over the near-side track, looking like an oddly askew hat. The shredded trunk of the tank commander remained sitting at his crew position, but his head had gone with the turret and his blood was spurting into the smoke-laden air.

There came a prrrt-prrrt from Stumm's MG-42 and a dozen Americans crumpled silently alongside their burning tank. Kreutzmann shoved an arm beneath the machine gun and scooped away a pile of empty cartridge cases, making room for more.

The battle had begun.

Prrrt-prrrt-prrrt! More falling bodies. More empty cartridge cases. But the Americans still kept coming. A section of them had set up a Browning heavy machine gun behind the burning tank, braving the explosion. To the right, others were lobbing grenades into the German forward positions. Medium calibre mortar bombs began to rain into the wood, accurately ranged and creating havoc amongst the reserve grenadier company. Now there came the clamour of heavy fighting on both flanks, as though the main thrust of the American armour had been

14

driven in two deep wedges astride the copse which had housed the 7·5cm PAK-41.

Helmut Kleiser stood by with the spare barrel of the MG-42 as the gun began to overheat. The American infantry piled in bloodied heaps under the hail of bullets from the rapid-firing Spandau. But mingled with their screams were determined shouts from officers and NCOs unwilling to fall back a second time.

But, then, the intensity of the German counter-barrage thickened, creeping closer to the American support lines, and with its thunder there also came the sound of other tank engines – the deep-throated roar of Mk V Panthers and Mk VI Tigers. At the same time, through the 3rd Company's forward lines came grenadiers of the 2nd Company, deployed in lines across the front, their sub-machine guns slung from their shoulders. Here was the counterattack which was to pin the Americans against the Wehrmacht counter-barrage!

The 3rd Company glimpsed these new arrivals out of the corners of their eyes and stepped up their rate of fire, to keep down the heads of the Americans until the counterattack got underway.

As the 2nd Company moved forward, Stumm and Kreutzmann lifted the loaded ammunition belts from about their necks and snatched up Kleiser's and Scherfe's G-41 Mauser rifles, both with bayonets fixed. Stumm prodded Kleiser with his boot and pointed to the MG-42. He didn't have to speak. Kleiser slid into position behind the gun, young Scherfe taking up the loaded belt at his side. Both knew well enough that Stumm and Kreutzmann had personal scores to settle with the Americans. Too many old mates from Grossdeutschland had died during the withdrawals of the past three months. They believed that these grenadiers hadn't survived the crippling winter frosts and the baking summer heat of the Russian steppes to be knocked off by some Errol Flynn hiding behind a tin crate which wouldn't last five minutes against a Panzer VI Tiger. The coming battle was personal and the hand-to-hand fighting it promised made it all the more personal. The division had been driven all the way from the Cotentin peninsula and through the hell of Falaise to this strip of woodland. Christ! But they'd got to dig their heels in somewhere – and that would be right here!

As the assault line of the 2nd Panzergrenadier Company rose to move forward, so Stumm and Kreutzmann joined them, advancing with them towards the Americans. They moved at a jog-trot, their hand weapons spraying the ground ahead of them. More Americans crumpled and the grenadiers stepped up the pace of their attack, charging through gaps between burning Shermans, some of them taking time to slot grenades through their open ports on the off-chance that there might still be crewmen inside who were prepared to fight to a finish.

During this phase and without armour reinforcements, the grenadiers had expected the American infantry to attempt to disengage and move tight against the counter-barrage, while leaving the ground clear for mortar and machine gun batteries. But the officers and NCOs were herding their men into defensive lines, where they stood firm to meet the threat with bayonets fixed. The panzergrenadiers rushed on with the spit of bullets and the scream of ricochets about their ears as the Americans began to return the fire with light and sub-machine guns. Still, the panzergrenadiers maintained the impetus of their attack, believing that when they got close enough for hand-to-hand fighting the Americans would either throw down their arms or stampede back to their own lines.

But they didn't . . .

The American line held and from the rear came the wild battle cries of the support troops who were racing across the shell-pitted earth to stand at their side.

Kreutzmann threw a quick glance at Stumm, but the lean, bearded profile told him nothing. He knew that their counter-assault wasn't going to plan. Green the Yanks might be, but they'd learned how to fight – and quick! This was not going to prove easy pickings.

A grenadier fell at his side. A bullet had slammed through one temple and passed through his brain, to blast off his steel helmet at the other side. He dropped at Kreutzmann's feet, but he barely glanced at the dead man; jerking up another round into the breech of the self-loading G-41 Mauser. In a bayonet skirmish a man needed one up the spout on the chance that the bayonet got itself stuck between the ribs of the enemy and had to be freed by shooting into the body. Men had died pointlessly by not taking that precaution!

Now they were in and amongst the Americans, and as Kreutzmann heaved aside a plunging bayonet and parried for his own thrust it struck him that these were young and healthy soldiers despite their battle tension. Their uniforms, though mud-stained and dripping water, were strong and tough compared with the threadbare grey-green they'd worn over the past year.

Kreutzmann's bayonet-thrust caught the man opposite him in the throat – too high! He could have missed altogether, but once the point had pierced the flesh he plunged it deep. The American's eyes bulged in their sockets and he clutched desperately at Kreutzmann's rifle barrel; but the German twisted it savagely in the wound and as the American's knees buckled he jabbed at his face with his jackboot, freeing the bayonet.

A new opponent confronted him, face ashen, a Thompson sub-machine gun held close to his chest. The man steadied himself, swinging down the muzzle before Kreutzmann could squeeze his own trigger. Kreutzmann knew he was too late and expected to see the tommy-gun belch death when the American suddenly keeled over, dropping lifelessly on to his face in the mud. Behind him, Klaus Stumm turned to another target.

There followed an insane sequence of stabbing, gouging, shooting, during which men of both armies died under the blows of rifle butts, entrenching tools, and the flat-blast of ·45-inch tommy-gun bullets which left a neat dry hole where they went in and a shredded bloody mess half the width of a man's body where they forced their way out.

It was becoming apparent to the Germans that, metre by metre, they were losing ground. The sheer weight of American infantry thrown against them in massive counterattacks was steam-rolling them back to the strip of woodland. And, as they fought with renewed desperation to stem the tide, so American armour began putting down a barrage of shell and small-arms fire, hindering their withdrawal. The Yanks had turned the tables.

There was only one thing the panzergrenadiers could do now if they were to survive – break and dash for their foxholes!

Now it was dark and the German positions were under a renewed and concentrated heavy artillery barrage. Rumours spread amongst the panzergrenadiers that General George Patton, himself, had visited the forward American positions and demanded to know what the hell the 5th Armoured Division was playing at. A frontline American point-division didn't get itself bogged down by a jaded, battle-fatigued, panzergrenadier regiment at a quarter of its strength and practically out of ammunition.

It was a good rumour, more than likely thought up by some panzer commander in an attempt to boost the flagging morale of the conscript reinforcements who had arrived from their training depot only three days earlier – eighteen-year-old kids wearing dead men's uniforms and carrying dead men's weapons.

But the weight of the new barrage gave the rumour some credence and the grenadiers cowered in their foxholes whilst the tide of high-explosive and flying shrapnel whizzed back and forth over their heads. Now and then, shrieking like a banshee, one of their number would leap from his slit-trench and madly race away under cover of the smoke of the last salvo. There was nothing anybody could do, for no man could stay alive under such a barrage. Only the screams of the hysterically demented few and the splashes of their blood carried on the wind of the explosions indicated that they had been there at all.

But the seasoned troops amongst them anticipated that the barrage would last all night and that with dawn the Americans would throw forward a mighty infantry and armoured attack. It looked as though there were to be no more half-measures – this was to be a savage and purposeful rejection of the usual American policy to minimise casualties. With first light would come the full strength of the 5th Armoured Division. Their Shermans would attempt to force a path through the thin cordon of panzergrenadiers, screwing them into their slit-trenches with their tracks, clearing a path for reconnaissance armoured cars to loop south-east and establish a new forward line which would seal off retreat to the Sarthe river. That would be the American objective. A man didn't have to be a bloody general to work it out for himself!

But shortly after one am the American barrage lifted a thousand metres to concentrate on the panzer laagers and reserve grenadier positions. Those in the forward lines were now able to stand up in their slit-trenches, stretch their aching limbs, remove the cottonwool from their buzzing ears, sip water from their bottles and turn out the last few hard-tack biscuits from their haversacks. But few moved far from the foxholes, aware that the sudden lift of the shelling could be no more than a ruse to entice them into the open. The additional danger of enemy infantry patrols infiltrating their positions caused those in the front lines to stand-to their weapons. Similarly, forward artillery observation officers kept their fingers on the triggers of their Kampfpistolen, ready to call down magnesium flares at the first hint of an American probe.

At two am, a runner from No 3 Company Headquarters came squirming through the mud to the forward positions.

'We're pulling out,' he hissed into Sturmann Klaus Stumm's ear. 'The forward line moves last . . .'

'Pulling out?' echoed Stumm. 'Christ! Whose decision is that?' He stared through the darkness, looking for officers. Then he turned back to the runner, wanting more information; but the man shrugged and began to crawl to the next foxhole to deliver the same message. On his way back he said over his shoulder, 'They say the Yanks have broken through to the north.'

Stumm's MG-42 machine gun section stood up in their foxhole. Sounds of movement already came from the rear. Mess tins clanking; the hard knock of metal against wooden rifle stocks; muttered obscenities; the squelch of jackboots in mud; the sharp helpless cries of wounded being shifted by inexperienced medics.

'Noisy bastards! Why don't they send the Yanks a telegram?'

The section crouched low, half-expecting to hear the impersonal chatter of a distant American machine gun and its bullets to come hissing through the trees. Bloody recruits! By the time they'd learned to be soldiers the war would be over – or they'd have died trying!

As they continued to watch, the hazy shapes of grenadiers in their coal-scuttle helmets could be seen rising out of their slit-trenches like the dead on resurrection day. They stretched their limbs, slung their weapons over their shoulders and began to edge their way over the shell-pitted ground to the rear.

As they blended into the darkness, Stumm motioned to his section and they, too, climbed out of the trench. Stumm unclipped the MG-42 from its tripod and heaved it over his shoulder. And when young Scherfe bent to drag the tripod from its emplacement, Stumm stabbed him with the toe of his boot.

'Leave it!' he said, 'unless you fancy carrying it all the way back to Berlin!'

Kreutzmann pulled a wry face. It was the first time he'd heard Stumm talk that way. It had always been "another pitch"! Another day! Another move back to better defensive positions – all part of a prepared plan by Oberkommando Wehrmacht which was to nip off the spearhead of the American armour. Never Berlin! Could it be that even Klaus Stumm, though nurtured by years of Grossdeutschland tradition, was at last beginning to change his views about the invincibility of the German Army? Berlin!

19

They came to the denser section of the wood where the panzers were laagered, still under heavy shellfire. The Panthers and the Tigers were hull-down in the soft earth, battened-up with the crews inside, prepared to tolerate the barrage until dawn when the overall battle situation could be more easily read. There was no point in making an impulsive move to the rear which could lead them into a direct confrontation with American detachments driving up from the south. The problem was there *was* no damned Intelligence! Scouting infantry patrols had been bogged down by the shelling and several had disappeared for all time.

The 3rd Company passed through the defensive circle of grenadiers dug in around the panzers and it was apparent that these troops had suffered heavy casualties. At times the American shelling had been so intense that there had been no chance to transport their wounded to forward field ambulance stations, and they lay in lines on the rain-soaked ground with new shrapnel bursts wounding them again and again.

Some of the less badly wounded hauled themselves to their feet with rifles used as crutches, calling to the men of the 3rd Company.

'Help me back, mate! Help me! See! I can walk! Help me for Christ's sake!'

But the withdrawing grenadiers didn't even turn their way, their eyes fixed on the pitted ground ahead, shoulders hunched against the buffeting of exploding shells.

The American artillery switched to star shells, evidently aware of the German withdrawal, and the magnesium flares floated sedately down to earth on their little parachutes.

But as the 3rd Company pressed on, so the shelling lost much of its intensity and, eventually the track along which they were marching broadened into a stone-strewn lane. Here it was punishing to cramped legs and feet, but the panzergrenadiers pushed forward, hoping that somewhere ahead they might find food and rest.

It was as they approached more woodland and the company reformed into column of rout that Sturmann Klaus Stumm slowed his pace. The three men of his section looked at him with speculative frowns, but he motioned them impatiently into single file behind him. And when they reached the first belt of dense pines he ushered them amongst the trees where they lay down and watched the rest of the company march out of sight.

Chapter Two

*Digest of a Communique issued by Oberkommando
Wehrmacht, Paris, to Reichsfuhrer Adolf Hitler
Date: 30th July 1944
Signatories:
Oberbefehlshaber West: Generalfeldmarschall
                          Gunther von Kluge
                          Generalfeldmarschall
                          Erwin Rommel*

*It is considered that the weakened German forces are no
longer capable of containing the 1st Canadian Army and the
2nd British Army (together constituting the 21st Army Group)
and the United States 1st and 3rd Armies (together constituting the United States 12th Army Group) within the lodgement
area of Normandy.*

*In consequence, orders for the withdrawal of the divisions of
Panzer Group West under the command of General Geyr von
Schweppenburg and the German 7th Army under the
command of General Dollmann have been issued.*

It had become apparent that with each passing day the situation in Normandy had become more desperate for the battle-
weary German armies. For, with each day, there came across
the Channel further Allied reinforcements: troops, tanks,
ammunition and stores. In contrast, German losses had long
since outweighed reinforcements to the extent that by the end
of July 1944, losses had exceeded over a hundred and twenty
thousand men, whereas replacements were below twenty
thousand!

Prior to von Kluge taking overall command of the German
forces in Normandy, it had been von Rundstedt's plan to
withdraw the German armies east, as far back as their own
Siegfried Line – the German West Wall. But Adolf Hitler had
refused point-blank to endorse such a plan and had insisted on
concentrating the main strength in Normandy to reinforce the

21

flank around the town of Caen. This not only weakened the German left southern flank, but was also a move which Field Marshal Bernard Montgomery, commander of the British 21st Army Group, had anticipated.

Up to this point, the United States 3rd Army, under the command of Lieutenant General George Smith Patton, had not been involved operationally in the Normandy battles and was standing-by to be launched in a highly mobile and decisive role.

This was a cleverly devised piece of strategy for, because of the 3rd Army's non-involvement, the Germans had no means of estimating its strength and striking power – until it was too late.

It subsequently transpired that the German forces on the southern flank (at the time constituting one panzer division, one infantry division and two security divisions) were too thin on the ground to halt Patton's spearhead.

However, in a desperate attempt to stem the swelling tide of the 3rd Army's advance, a German battle group was rapidly formed from units of the 17th SS Panzergrenadier Division and from the 2nd SS Panzer Division. But, by this time, the German left flank no longer reached to the Channel and their defensive wall to the south had been cracked wide open.

Sergeant Joe Lavanski, commanding the point No 2 Troop of No 3 Squadron of the Second Regiment of the United States 5th Armoured Division, sat meditatively on the rim of the turret of his Sherman. The armoured patrol had halted at the outbreak of the star-shelling and they'd pulled into the side of the lane, suddenly vulnerable to any SS lunatic with a panzerfaust or a sticky grenade. This was no time to be brave!

The rain had stopped and as the minutes passed he could sense the 30-ton Sherman sinking inch-by-inch on its left track into the soft verge. It wouldn't be wise to stay here too long, either.

Most of that day they'd swanned thirty or forty kilometres south of the town of Laval with the tumult of the battle to the north ringing in their ears. There had been little doubt that the main thrust-force of the 5th Armoured were having a rough time; but, all the same, the flanking squadrons couldn't just stand around and wait. Whether Patton broke through or not, they had to complete their flanking movement and get themselves into a position to nip off any elements of the 2nd or 17th SS Panzer Divisions which were still mobile enough to make a suicide dash for the bridges over the Sarthe river. So far they'd come upon scant resistance. US reconnaissance regiments had roared along the country roads of Normandy, meeting little apart from the occasional enemy scout car and one despatch rider whom they'd gunned from his saddle before he'd realised that these tanks weren't German.

Now they were close in on their own shelling. The recce patrols had moved farther south, scouting for lightly-held secondary roads, acutely aware that the as yet uncommitted 14th SS Panzer Division was racing from the south to intercept. Ultimately, this final push to the Sarthe could prove dicey!

Sergeant Joe Lavanski, with the situation firmly in his mind and the whole of the US 5th Armoured Division strung out behind him, reckoned that this was one of the few times when it would be prudent to await developments from the enemy. His best plan was to radio for immediate infantry support and put out a patrol farther to the north. In his own mind he was convinced that his spearhead had bumped into the main axis of enemy withdrawal, but he had no way of assessing its strength. It would be stupid to commit even a couple of his tanks which, in the kind of chain reaction which could follow, might involve his troop in a full-scale battle at a point of the enemy's choosing.

He picked up the radio handset from its hook on the side of the turret: 'Hello, Sunray! Hello, Sunray! This is Sunray One . . . do you read me? This is Sunray One . . .'

His voice tailed off as he spotted four uniformed figures making their way into the shadows of a wood maybe half a mile ahead. They were moving unhurriedly, in single file, and the leading man had what looked like an MG-42 machine gun slung over his shoulder. Lavanski had had no idea they'd got so close to the Krauts!

Sturmann Klaus Stumm led his section deeper into the dense woodland, stumbling over roots and tree stumps in the darkness.

In addition to their personal equipment and weapons, Kreutzmann, Kleiser and Scherfe had loaded ammunition belts for the MG-42 slung about their necks – heavy, unwieldy lengths which weighed like anchor chains and caught about their legs, bayonet scabbards, and water bottles.

Some time earlier, they had run into trouble which had compelled them to switch direction farther to the north. About two kilometres from the point at which they'd deserted the 3rd Company, they'd come upon more American shelling, intensified in support of an aerial bombardment on second-line Wehrmacht reinforcements. It was immediately apparent that no precautions had been taken against the possibility of an attack of such dimensions so far behind the forward lines, and by the time it *had* developed it was too late to do anything about it.

Stumm and his section had given the scene of the carnage a wide berth, keeping to the higher slopes above the valley, looking down on the chaos astride the narrow winding road, brightly illuminated by burning vehicles and exploding ammunition trucks. Such horrors weren't new to them but, all the same, they halted and squatted amongst the trees, watching.

The dead and wounded had been abandoned where they lay, many with their clothing still smouldering; here and there the shadowy figures of stretcher-bearers could be seen moving in and out of the flames. Odd ranging shells were still dropping accurately amongst the destruction, and with each whoosh-whoosh in the air the shadowy figures flattened themselves to the ground against the dull crump of the explosion. It was a demoralising scene. If the Americans could cause this kind of devastation from a distance of eleven or twelve kilometres, and without committing a single tank or infantryman, then what could the future hold for any of them?

'Let's get out of here!'

Stumm snarled the words impulsively, levering himself to his feet with the MG-42. The rest of the section adjusted the ammunition belts about their necks, eased the sharp points of the bullets away from their flesh and also got to their feet.

They were on the point of moving off when a sudden burst of small-arms fire down in the valley grabbed their attention. Groups of soldiers armed with what, at that distance, appeared to be sub-machine guns, were winkling men out of the trees on to the wreckage-strewn road. They were jabbing at them with the butts of their weapons and over the distance there came the noise of their commands followed by the quick obscenities of the others.

Kreutzmann nudged Stumm.

'Would you say that could be the start of a mutiny?'

Stumm halted again, binoculars to his eyes. Then he shrugged, slinging the MG-42 back over his shoulder.

'They've made a start by killing off the officers,' he said

24

unemotionally. 'We'd best get out of here. We don't want to be identified with that pack!'

They moved on, turning up the slope, widening the distance but with eyes still on the massacre in the valley.

Stumm had been right! A group of men without helmets had been lined up alongside one of the burning trucks, whilst another group covered them with sub-machine guns. A man went down the line collecting what could have been dog-tags and tossing them on to the flames.

Then a couple of soldiers came forward with MG-42s slung from their shoulders on their straps and machine-gunned the line of prisoners. Others threw the corpses on to the same burning truck.

Minutes later the survivors, about twenty strong, gathered together in a tight group and, leaving the wounded where they lay, began to pick their way up the other side of the valley.

Young Rudi Scherfe, pale-faced and incredulous at what he had just witnessed, asked, 'They won't get away with it, will they Sturmann?'

At that Stumm jerked out a laugh. 'What's it matter, anyway?' he asked. 'Do you want to go down there an' take a look round? Pick up a few regimental flashes? Make out a report to OKW? That's all right with me. Go ahead! Give Kleiser your ammo belt.'

Scherfe glanced at Helmut Kleiser out of the corner of his eye as he dropped into single file behind the big man. He was thinking that maybe he'd been a bloody fool to have followed Stumm even this far. There was no telling where the man was leading them and, judging by what he'd seen of him during the past couple of months, there were many reasons to question his sanity. One of the problems was that it was impossible to communicate with the man, for he rarely spoke – apart from the kind of pitying sarcasm he'd used just now about the killing in the valley.

Also, whether he was manning his MG-42 in some foxhole or whiling away his day in a rest area, he invariably appeared to be in some kind of mental haze. Like a cat. Better still – a panther! Inscrutable and with all the venom and hate bred in five endless years of privation, maiming and killing locked behind those slitted, pale-blue eyes.

Stumm wasn't even a good leader. During the short time Scherfe had served with the section it had been apparent that the sturmann didn't give a damn for anybody but himself. Perhaps once or twice, in one of his sharp curt sentences, he had wanted to know how his pal Franz Kreutzmann was making out. But that was only because Kreutzmann had almost died from a chest wound somewhere beyond the Russian Dnieper and Scherfe believed that Stumm was worried about who would feed the MG-42 if Kreutzmann flaked out in action! As for Kleiser and himself, well, they could fry alive under a napalm squirt and he wouldn't lift a finger to help. A fighting animal! An out and out self-centred bastard with the bravado of a showman! Scherfe didn't know whether he'd more to fear from Sturmann Klaus Stumm than he had from the Americans. The truth was that Stumm was fast nearing his breaking point and when that happened a lot of people were going to get hurt – and they wouldn't all be American!

Despite his wounds, Kreutzmann was a different kind of man, for the war hadn't knocked him sideways as it had Stumm. There'd been times, not many, but times when he'd confided in Kleiser and Scherfe about a family home somewhere near Oestrich-Rheingau. That scrap of information had jolted Scherfe for he'd been no more able to imagine Kreutzmann with a young wife and small son than he had Klaus Stumm. But it was true, for Kreutzmann had pulled a faded snapshot from his tunic pocket showing the man himself wearing a neatly-pressed uniform with the Gothic-script cuff-titles of the Grossdeutschland Division. These he had positioned to face the camera, but there was also a pretty dark-haired girl standing beside him holding a young baby in her arms. Neither Scherfe nor Kleiser had known what to say, but it immediately became apparent that Kreutzmann hadn't expected comments, for he snatched the snapshot from Kleiser and shoved it back into his tunic pocket with neither a word nor a change of expression. Yet that simple act had indicated to Scherfe that somewhere deep in Kreutzmann's secret self their lurked a love for his small family – but that was all it said! What it didn't say was whether Kreutzmann ever expected to see them again and, if he did happen to survive the war, what his plans were for them in the peace ahead. Neither did it in any way indicate that the reason Kreutzmann was fighting this war was for those two innocent people in the snapshot.

But Rudi Scherfe didn't care. Nor did he discuss the possibility with Kleiser, who was nothing more than a gnat-brained farmhand who'd been held in a reserved occupation until 1942.

Since his call-up, Kleiser had once told him, he'd been

stationed on the northern coast of France, mainly along the Pas de Calais with the 317th Infantry Regiment which had been mustered from veterans of the 1914—18 war, young boys weeks out of school cadet-corps, and late conscripts like himself.

Thus, knowing little to start with, Kleiser had learned little more during his years manning bunkers and machine gun strongpoints along the 'Iron Coast' of France. It had just been his bad luck that his very first posting had come through on 1 June 1944, transferring him to Vierville-sur-Mer a mere five days before the United States 1st Infantry Division landed there and code-named it 'Omaha Beach'.

But this *did* mean that of the men in Sturmann Klaus Stumm's MG-42 machine gun section, Kleiser had fought longest in Normandy; for only when the 4th Panzer Army had begun to wilt against constantly increasing American pressure had detachments of seasoned veterans been rushed to put backbone into the depleted German divisions.

Thus, Stumm and Kreutzmann had seen no more than two months' action in Normandy. This was a fact which Kleiser had grown to cherish and about which he boasted to Scherfe from time to time. But he'd said nothing about it to Stumm or Kreutzmann, and Scherfe knew that he would never dare. Knowing how Stumm hated Kleiser's guts, that caused Scherfe to smile!

Even so, Scherfe had often wished that Kleiser had been intelligent enough to talk on more serious matters; for, as things were, Scherfe found himself out on a limb. There wasn't a man in whom he could confide — not even about his family problems — and that could be bloody difficult for a boy still three months away from his eighteenth birthday! Six weeks ago, he wouldn't have believed that homicidal killers like Klaus Stumm would have been allowed to hold rank in the German Army. Least of all that it would be his lot to serve under such a man! Already, Stumm had taught him how to kill easily and without remorse. He'd even kept a score. Six! He'd already killed six men for certain: five Americans and one French civilian he'd mistaken for a Resistance fighter.

The death of the Frenchman worried him no more than that of the Americans. What really twisted his mind were the images of his mother and two younger sisters which he sensed, in some mysterious way, hovering above him as he lay petrified with fear at the bottom of his water-logged foxhole. What would his mother think if she were to learn that her only son had killed six human beings — and in less than two months? The thought sapped his strength, for it was no use telling himself that less than four months ago he'd been a schoolboy, because most of the reinforcement conscripts in his age group could make identical claims. Even so, his waking moments, as well as his sleep, were haunted by the ghosts of those American boys who'd crossed four thousand miles of ocean to die at his hands.

He was to have been an architect. An architect! Wasn't that a bloody laugh? There had been times, even during the nerve-snapping horror of his first battle, when he'd believed there was just a chance he might survive the war — but that had been before he was posted to Sturmann Klaus Stumm's MG-42 machine gun section. Now there wasn't a cat in hell's chance! He also had a sneaking feeling that Kreutzmann might be thinking the same way. Only the thick-headed farmhand, Helmut Kleiser, could leer his way idiot-fashion through a battle, convinced he was bound to come out at the other end happy and smiling.

The section trudged on, climbing higher into the trees to the north side of the valley, slithering over mud and loose stones, water cascading upon them with each sapling they stirred. Yet, at Stumm's insistence, they moved operationally; wary of marauding French Resistance fighters who would now be forming themselves into battle groups ahead of the American advance. These would be men with a determination to kill boiling the blood in their veins, intent on avenging the murder and torture of their fellow-countrymen at the hands of the Gestapo and the Waffen SS. There would be no exception made — all Germans were Germans and all Germans were bastards who'd to be killed slowly. Very slowly! These Germans running from the American spearhead must be made to atone for all that France had suffered during four years of occupation. At long last, the Resistance was about to use the teeth it had sharpened for so long!

There were also Bulgarians, Czechs, Rumanians, Yugo-Slavs and even Russians who had been drafted into the Wehrmacht as soon as the tide of battle had swung away from them. These men, like those who had just murdered their officers in the valley, would also probably be running wild in the midst of the retreating Germans; at long last able to bait the lion which had tormented them for so many months — scabs of a German house-painter who'd taken their women, their children, their homes and their land.

Germans seeking crossing points to the east bank of the Sarthe river would only find safety in strength. Odd detachments would be easy prey for these marauding bands. But every German could still make his choice: turn round and face the US 3rd Army or head east into the ambushes of the war-savaged flotsam of Europe. Sturmann Klaus Stumm had made that decision and now he'd make sure that his section would follow.

They marched on, beyond the crest of the range and down a gentle slope into yet another tree-filled valley. The rain had begun again and a low covering of clouds had blanked out the quarter-moon, making the night as black as it had ever been. The section pulled out gas capes from their haversacks and threw them over their shoulders, but the rain streamed from their steel helmets to find its way inside their tunic collars, picking icy tracks down their backs like dead men's fingers. A sudden chill which permeated the night belied this French late summer, carried along a rising wind from the north-east, soughing through the trees and bulging out the oiled material of their gas capes.

Presently they reached an escarpment of rocky outcrop which dropped sheer, thirty of forty metres, and Stumm led them down grabbing at small trees and shrubs to steady themselves over the slippery rock. Stumm was having difficulty with the MG-42, but he turned on Kleiser angrily when the big man offered to take it.

It was at the base of the escarpment that they came upon a barn. This hadn't been visible until they were almost upon it for it was a grey-painted structure, built halfway underneath an overhanging ledge of outcrop with shrubs planted at either side, as though it had been intentionally camouflaged into the hillside.

Stumm motioned Kleiser forward. The big man hesitated momentarily, wary of what he might find in the dark building; but Stumm jabbed the muzzle of the Spandau into his backside and Kleiser reluctantly moved forward, images of an armed band of Resistance fighters buzzing around in his mind. He glanced back at Stumm, as though expecting a change of orders, but Stumm angrily motioned him inside.

Kleiser lifted the latch slowly and then impulsively lashed out at the wooden door with the flat sole of his boot. It swung fully round on its hinges and he dashed inside as he'd been taught at the street-fighting school. He tore across the open space, then turned abruptly with his back to the wall, finger tight against the trigger of his rifle.

29

But the place was empty. Kleiser remained where he was, eyes straining into the farthest and darkest corners, then lifting them to a second floor which covered the rear half of the barn and was piled high with hand-tied bales of hay. There was also a roughly-made ladder propped against the ledge and Kleiser strode across and kicked it to the floor. Finally, he came back to the door and peered outside, picking out the three hazy shapes of the section against the outcrop ten metres away.

'It's empty, Sturmann!' he called with a surge of elation in his voice. He could just as easily have been a mangled corpse by now, caught in the crossfire of French Resistance bullets! 'Good place for a kip. Plenty of hay . . .'

But when Stumm approached him, Kleiser saw that his eyes were hard and there was a savage twist to his lips. Stumm was thinking that Kleiser had been shit-scared of going into that barn, as well as being a bloody fool shouting across the yard when he'd come out!

'Then you can do the first guard stint,' he growled. 'Give young Scherfe a knock in a couple of hours!'

François Riand was nine-years-old and he awoke early that morning. With the dawn bright and clear after the storm of the previous night, he clambered across his counterpane to a small window set high in the gable end of the farmhouse and drew back the blue gingham curtains. Little François loved to wake early on a summer's morning, for there above the farmyard he could watch the animals leisurely beginning their day. He could also look across to the woods, which bordered the escarpment on that side of the house, from where the birds would fill the valley with their dawn chorus. That's how it was this morning! There were three larks above the big meadow, and over the valley to the left of the escarpment a lone kestrel was hovering silently: breathtakingly still. The little boy watched it wide-eyed, until it swooped in a golden-brown blur upon its unsuspecting prey.

He turned back to the escarpment and its grey wooden barn where he and Jules, his friend from along the lane, spent most of their summer holidays together. With a snap of their fingers they could miraculously change it from an outpost in the Maginot Line to one of the American B-29 Flying Fortress bombers they'd glimpsed high in the sky several times that week.

Now that the war was getting closer it was becoming all the more exciting and both he and Jules were looking forward to the day when they would see, for the first time, American soldiers racing down the escarpment.

How the Boches would run!

Papa had told him the Boches would run and he'd been a soldier, too, until he'd come home to look after Maman and the farm. Since then the Boches had taken most of their produce, but Papa still looked after the farm whilst Maman made butter, cheese, and baked bread. Papa had said that when the Americans chased the Boches away, all the good things which Maman made would be theirs to keep!

Suddenly, he started.

There was somebody standing on the cobbles in front of the barn! It was a man, but he wore no hat and he was opening his trousers and peeing on to the cobbles. Little François frowned. Papa wouldn't like that! Unhealthy, he always said. Only animals did things like that. The man, whoever he was, should have gone into the trees.

He called.

'Papa! Papa!'

No answer. He glanced at the old alarm clock propped on his dressing table by the foot of his bed.

Quarter-past-four!

He called again.

'Papa! Papa!'

This time a sleepy voice answered, lightly irritable.

'Yes, Frankie! What is it?'

'Papa! There's a man at the barn!'

'A man?' Sharper now. 'What kind of man?'

François shrugged to himself. What kind of man? What did Papa mean? Just a man! And why had Maman suddenly gasped like that?

'Just a man,' he replied. 'He was peeing!'

Seconds later there came the clomp of heavy footsteps up the wooden stairs to François' room and his father opened the door. The boy was surprised to see that, apart from his boots, he was already dressed and that he was carrying a shotgun in one hand and a bundle of cartridges in the other. A sudden dart of fear clouded his young healthy face.

'What is the matter, Papa . . .?'

But Jean-Michel Riand only smiled down at his small son, rumpling his hair with the hand which held the cartridges.

'Maman says you're to go along to her, Frankie,' he said gently. 'Right now. She'll give you a cuddle before it's time to get up. Now, off you go!'

31

The boy looked doubtful but he slipped obediently from his bed, pausing only to seek further reassurance from his father's smiling face before scampering across the room in his long blue and white nightshirt to his parents' room on the floor below.

Franz Kreutzmann buttoned up his trousers and looked about him contemplatively before going back into the barn. The sun was already brightening and the Normandy countryside looked rich and lush with the large meadows spreading across the valley in their patterns of green and brown. He was thinking that soon, maybe, they'd have a chance to dry out their uniforms and clean their weapons. That would be some comfort, for no one had done more than doze fitfully during the three hours they'd been at the barn.

It was then that he spotted a man approaching. He was a youngish man, probably in his early thirties, with a full beard and long black hair which spread over the collar of his denim shirt. He was very suntanned and there was a frown of concentration furrowing his brow as he stared into the sun, searching the ground ahead. He also carried a shotgun at the hip, military fashion. It was only then that Kreutzmann noticed the steeply-angled gable end of a house beyond the tall elms to the west. There was also a tiny window up there, almost at the apex. Unhurriedly, he slipped back into the barn, leaving the door open and climbing up the shaky ladder to the hay loft. He tugged gently at Stumm's boot.

Stumm blinked the sleep from his eyes, momentarily eased some of the cramp from his limbs and stretched painfully in his damp clothing before giving Kreutzmann his attention. Too experienced to make a sound, he lifted his eyebrows.

Kreutzmann spoke in little more than a whisper. 'Armed man on his way here, Klaus. There's a house about a half-kilometre away. Maybe that's the farmhouse'.

Stumm sat up, sliding on his backside over the hay to the ladder. He motioned in the direction of the sleeping bodies of Kleiser and Scherfe. Kreutzmann nodded. He'd see they kept quiet.

Stumm climbed down the ladder as though he had all the time in the world and when he reached the door he saw that the man with the gun was not a hundred metres away. His expression eased. This was a civilian. Some bloody French peasant! And he'd been thinking that he might be a forward scout for some Yank infantry patrol. Looked as though his section had

32

come farther than they'd intended in the rain! Now the only sound of gunfire came from farther to the west. Could be that both sides had taken time off to count their casualties.

He went back into the barn, moving behind the open door, and seconds later when Jean-Michel Riand strode boldly into the building, Kreutzmann called out to him from the hayloft. And, as the Frenchman reacted to the sound, so Stumm buried his knife up to the hilt in the man's back. This was no wild, sudden stab, but one struck with the precision of a surgeon which pierced the heart to the ribs beyond.

Jean-Michel Riand was dead before he touched the floor.

Stumm stood over him, letting the man's weight free the knife, then stooping to wipe the blood from the blade on his denim shirt. He slipped it back into its scabbard and called up to Kreutzmann.

'Wake those idle buggers up, Franz! Now we know where we can find some breakfast!'

Madeleine Riand had dressed quickly after her husband had left the house, at the same time urging her small son into his clothes. She could sense the new dangers ahead now that the war was almost at their doorstep. Scores of unheard horrors could be threatening them, but on the other hand she had also heard of families who'd lived close to the invasion beaches and these people and their homes had somehow managed to escape destruction. Now they were safe far behind the enemy lines and for them the war was over.

She had prayed that her small family might be equally lucky. She and her husband had worked twelve hours a day over the past three years, cutting this small farmstead from the surrounding outcrop and woodland. Surely it was their right to enjoy some of the fruits of their labour?

But here was the first threat! The first indication that intruders were about – and she was taking no chances.

In the kitchen she cut thick slices of bread and spread them with butter. These she put in a paper bag with a piece of cold sausage from the cellar and handed the bag to her son.

'You've to go to Tante Marie, François,' she told him. 'You must go right away. And don't stop to talk to anyone. Just go as quickly as you can!'

'But why, Maman?' he asked plaintively. 'I want to see the Americans. Please let me stay!'

But she shook her head emphatically and bundled him through the door, pointing along the path that led to the east and her sister's farm two kilometres beyond the hill.

She watched his small figure trudge reluctantly down the path, and after he had turned to wave before disappearing into the trees she went back into the farmhouse. It was impossible to see the barn from there and she had half a mind to go up to the boy's room and take a look; but no sounds came from over the distance and the silence encouraged her. Had Jean-Michel been suspicious he would either have called or fired his shotgun.

Kleiser and Scherfe led the way into the farmyard; Sturmann Stumm not risking the whole of his section moving across open ground together. There was no telling who might be laagered up at that farm. Kleiser and Stumm would know what to do if they happened to bump into any Americans. Safer to keep to an operational fire-and-movement drill.

Madeleine Riand spotted them from her kitchen window. The heavy, lumbering Helmut Kleiser with a week's growth of beard bristling from his round, florid, face. A pair of small, deep-set eyes beneath the rim of his coal-scuttle helmet.

At his side, the tall and lightly-built Rudi Scherfe, young, alert.

Both with sub-machine guns at the ready. Both poised on the balls of their feet to dive for cover at the first threat.

The woman watched them approach with heart racing. Fresh in her mind were stories she'd heard from neighbours, by way of the Resistance, of the kind of horrors to which French civilians had been subjected by half-crazed German deserters. There had been an eye-witness to the holocaust at Oradour-sur-Glan, where a whole community of over six hundred people — men, women and children — had been pitilessly murdered in a three-hour period of unparalleled butchery, during which the women and children had been burned alive in the village church. This was no anti-Nazi propaganda myth. This was fact! She had personally known some of the people who'd perished in Oradour-sur-Glan!

But, on the other hand, there were also rumours that most of the Wehrmacht battalions were now being formed from ex-Volksturm — homeguard conscripts — and boys fresh from school; neither of whom wanted more than to return to their families in Germany. Anyway, Madeleine Riand told herself, the Americans could only be a few kilometres away. The noise of their heavy guns beyond the hills to the west was growing louder with every new day.

Besides, Jean-Michel would be back home any minute now. He'd learned to speak German fluently during his year at the

34

prisoner-of-war camp. He'd know what to do.

Even so, as the two panzergrenadiers crossed the yard to the house she took a long look back into the room, contemplating whether she should make her escape by the back door and follow her son to her sister's home. But she shied at leaving her husband. Perhaps it would be wiser to brave things out until Jean-Michel returned . . .

Her mind made up she went out to meet the Germans, face blank and her morale lifting at the sight of their haggard, ill-kempt appearance. The Americans must have been giving them hell! Now the animals were beaten! Scuttering back to their Fatherland and, this time, not goose-stepping in that stupid arrogant way they had!

'We shall not hurt you, Madame! We seek only food!'

This from the younger of the two soldiers, the fair-haired boy who looked as though he should still have been at school. Up closer, even the big man looked amiable enough as he moved along like some shaggy bear. Her worries eased. She could be human enough to give food even to the *sales* Boches!

'There is bread and cheese and a little wine,' she said.

Their faces brightened and the big man turned to signal to the copse below the barn; whereupon, two more soldiers came into the open. One, a lean gaunt man, was carrying a machine gun over his shoulder. The other, pale and limping, appeared to be ill and even at that distance she could detect the strain in his face. Her recent optimism vanished and a worried frown crossed her brow as she asked herself where Jean-Michel could be. She lifted her eyes again to the distance, but the ill-looking soldier distracted her.

'We'd like the bread and cheese, Madame! If you're looking for your husband, he went on into the wood!'

She moved ahead of them into the farmhouse, revolted by the stench of their bodies and the cloying stains on their uniforms. There was something about their eyes, too, which unnerved her — even those of the fair-haired boy. She took a large bottle of wine from a cupboard beneath the window and placed it on the table with four glasses. The big man who had been first into the yard wasted no time in pouring, handing the first glass to the man with the machine gun. Now she *was* worried about Jean-Michel, but she daren't speak. She went out into the pantry and returned with a large circular loaf and a hunk of cheese.

These she placed on the table alongside the wine bottle and hurried to the door which led to the farmyard.

'Where're you going?'

Sturmann Stumm's sharp question pulled her up short and she froze where she stood before turning round slowly.

She made an effort to shrug indifference.

'There is milking to do . . .'

He jabbed a forefinger at one of the chairs.

'You sit down!'

She nodded, and perched herself on the edge of the chair, waiting, watching this German scum tear at the food like the animals they were. Scum! Boches scum! Jackals of a defeated army, now only capable of preying on defenceless families! Animals like the ones who'd devastated Oradour-sur-Glan! Oradour-sur-Glan . . .? Her face paled as she realised in which direction her contempt had been leading her. Oradour! Where was Jean-Michel? Holy Mother . . . Please . . . Where was Jean-Michel?

The gaunt man got to his feet and as he did so he swung a fist to knock the hunk of bread from the big man's hand.

'We got things to do besides eat, Kleiser,' he growled without raising his voice. 'Take the woman upstairs!'

Madeleine Riand shrank within herself, clinging to the wooden arms of her chair, but the big man dragged her to her feet without effort. There was a grin on his heavy face which told her he was enjoying himself and she spun her head in a desperate appeal to the others. But the man with the machine gun had his eyes fixed on the man holding her. The one with the limp was disinterestedly rolling a cigarette. The young boy was watching the tableau as though he wasn't really a part of it. She snatched at her only chance of salvation and called to him.

'Please! Please! I am a wife and mother . . . Please! For pity's sake, help me!'

Her voice rose to a scream, but the fair-haired boy didn't even stir in his chair and continued to watch as though her cries had been part of that same tableau. Kleiser half-carried her out of the room with a great arm clamped about her body, a hand over her breast.

It was when they heard him stumbling up the wooden stairs to the first floor that Stumm shoved back his chair.

'This won't take long, Franz,' he said to Kreutzmann as he passed him. 'Keep an eye on the escarpment!'

Upstairs they spread-eagled Madeleine Riand on the large bed and Kleiser lashed her wrists and ankles to the bedposts with curtain cord.

'I had a mate in Kursk who got himself castrated with a

razorblade by some Russian whore,' Stumm commented and Kleiser grinned all over his face, flattered that the sturmann had bothered to talk to him.

'Can't be too careful,' he agreed.

'Then get yourself lost!'

'What?'

'Are you deaf as well as bloody ignorant you ungainly fat sod! I said get lost!'

Kleiser's hackles rose in much the same way as they had that time when Stumm had flicked the loaded ammunition belt at him during the first salvoes of the American barrage. His small eyes flashed their venom but, all the same, he went dutifully to the door and closed it behind him.

Stumm stooped over the woman and pulled out the wad which Kleiser had wedged in her mouth to silence her.

White-faced and wild-eyed she spat up into his face.

'Boche pig! Pig! Pig!'

Stumm took his knife from his belt and meticulously placed the point of the blade a centimetre below her left eye. He pressed and a spot of bright blood appeared.

'Say what you like,' he told her. 'You've nothing more to lose. Your man's dead. He barged into the barn!'

She was screaming her denial as he ran the blade through her clothing, cutting through the denim of her dress, through her underwear, making a clean incision into her skin which ran down between her breasts, over her navel to the hair at the top of her legs, oozing blood along its length. Now she no longer appeared to be aware of what was happening to her. Through a haze she saw this beast of a German loosening his tunic, opening his trousers. More positive was the stench of the man and the sudden squirt of semen within seconds of his entering her. He slid off her, looking down at her naked body with its long knife wound. He was thinking that maybe he'd wait until he was ready again, but the woman fainted and vomited onto the pillow beside her.

He crossed to the door and bellowed down the steps.

'Kleiser! Kleiser!'

'Sturmann!'

'Your turn!'

'Me?' There was incredulity in his voice.

'Yeh! You! Who else?'

Kleiser came up the stairs two at a time, stroking his erection through the material of his trousers, but when he neared the top he backed against the wall to make room for

37

Stumm, who passed him without a glance.

Once at the bottom of the stairs, Stumm called him again.
'Kleiser!'

'Sturmann!'

'You mightn't like what you find up there, but when you've finished whatever you do, see you cut her throat!'

The grin of anticipation faded from Kleiser's face.

'Cut her throat?'

'That's what I said, isn't it? Or do you want your description given to the Resistance? A slob like you wouldn't be difficult for 'em to trace!'

Still Kleiser hesitated.

'Is that an order, Sturmann?'

'Yeh! That's an order, Kleiser!' Then, turning back into the room. 'Scherfe!'

'Sturmann!'

'Take a look round upstairs. See what that dumb sod's up to!'

Rudi Scherfe got up from his chair and picked up the loaded Schmeiser. Somehow, he'd managed to close his eyes and ears to what had happened since they'd come across the barn under the escarpment. None of it had really happened. Stumm hadn't killed the French farmer. Nor had he raped his wife. Kleiser hadn't just gone upstairs to cut her throat!

All the same, he went upstairs as Stumm had ordered, wasting time on the landing and listening to Kleiser grunting and shuffling about in the bedroom. But he didn't open the door. On his right was another door which he did open — wasting more time — but this was nothing more than a small storeroom fitted with shelves on which stood bottled fruit and vegetables. At the end of the corridor were more stairs, steeper and narrower. Scherfe slung the Schmeiser over his shoulder and went up, to find a small room built into the eaves at the apex of the gable. Inside was a cot bed with a patchwork counterpane, a table, a chest of drawers and a dressing table on which stood a few wooden toys.

He hurried down to the living room again and told Stumm what he had found.

The sturmann reacted violently: 'A child, you say? Then where is it? Where?'

Scherfe looked blank. 'Gone, Sturmann!'

'Gone where, for Christ's sake?'

Scherfe shook his head helplessly.

'The room's empty, Sturmann!'

Stumm turned to glower at Kreutzmann.

'Unless we find the kid, we can't hang on here. Scherfe! Go get Kleiser moving . . .' When Scherfe hesitated, Stumm brought the flat of his hand down hard on the table top. 'I mean now!'

Scherfe turned back to the stairs. There was still noise coming from the room, but all of it from the man.

'Kleiser!' Scherfe shouted and when there was no answer he banged against the door with the butt of the Schmeiser. 'Kleiser! We're pulling out!'

With that he flung open the door, prepared to go inside, but he halted abruptly at the threshold. Kleiser was standing by the bed with his trousers at his ankles, his heavy penis limp, his arms and thighs red with blood. There was a kommando knife in his right hand and, even as Scherfe watched, he again slashed viciously at the dead body of the woman.

'She laughed at me!' he cried in a curiously high-pitched voice. 'The French tart laughed at me!'

Scherfe turned away.

'Stumm wants you right away,' he said. 'I should move it! He's not in a mood for waiting.'

They packed their haversacks with bread and cheese from the larder and filled their water bottles with what remained of the wine. Then they moved out into the yard, orientating themselves by the rumble of gunfire which was closer now, deciding in which direction to move. Inevitably, it could only be northeast and, as Stumm had commented to Kreutzmann, they couldn't risk staying on at the farm with the kid running about loose. Maybe a French Resistance squad was already being assembled to march on them. Bloody bad luck! But all they could do was move on!

They turned back into the wood, avoiding paths and fire breaks which criss-crossed at intervals. Kleiser and Scherfe were leading and some twenty metres apart, with Stumm and Kreutzmann together forming the third angle of the triangle. No one spoke. Scherfe still introspective, dwelling on what he'd witnessed that morning; Kleiser with the taunts of the Frenchwoman still ringing in his ears; Kreutzmann, his old wounds giving him hell, struggling through the thickening undergrowth and acutely aware that his strength was failing; Stumm wondering if he'd have been wiser hanging on with the 3rd Company until they'd got across the Sarthe. One thing was for certain, anyway, Stumm told himself: no bugger could get them for desertion! All they'd to do was tag on to the next column they came across and claim they'd lost contact during last night's battle. He grinned sardonically to himself. Hell of a way for a Grossdeutschland NCO to start thinking, that was! But this was beginning to look like the withdrawal from Voronezh all over again!

Ahead, Scherfe had halted at the edge of a copse, his rifle held above his head.

Stumm and Kreutzmann caught up with him.

Scherfe pointed down the slope into the valley.

'You hear engines, Sturmann?' he said. 'Sounds like trucks. Soft-skinned stuff.'

Stumm beckoned to Kleiser.

'Take a look down there! See what's moving?'

Kleiser glared, wanting to ask, 'Why me again?' but all he did was shamble off into the undergrowth with his rifle touching the trail and his Schmeiser slung across his body.

Scherfc and Kreutzmann unhooked the heavy MG-42 ammunition belts from about their necks and sank down on to the thick turf next to Stumm, lighting cigarettes, eyes fixed on the route Kleiser had taken. From the far west there came the throb-throb of aircraft engines and they guessed these could only be US fighter-bombers strafing the few remaining suicide squads of the Wehrmacht rearguard. Farther to the south there was also a distant drone of engines. Panzers? Tanks? Could be either Tigers or Shermans. At such a distance they were impossible to identify.

About ten minutes later there was movement in the bushes ahead and the ungainly figure of Helmut Kleiser emerged. He had taken off his helmet and there were purple weals across his forehead where the leather lining had bitten into his skin.

He was streaming perspiration and his lip curled as he looked scathingly at Scherfe.

'Soft-skinned vehicles my arse! Stupid young sod! They're Yank armoured cars. Dozens of the bastards!' He paused and swung round to Stumm. 'Looks as though we're behind the enemy lines, Sturmann!'

Chapter Three

Sergeant Joe Lavanski's No 2 Troop of No 3 Squadron of the Second Regiment of the United States 5th Armoured Division was still at the point — as Lavanski had reported: 'with the whole goddamn US Army stretched out behind us!'

During the hours of darkness, whilst the main force of US armour and infantry had been hammering the German panzer divisions to the south-west, trucks had come forward with gasoline and the troops' Shermans had been refuelled and rearmed. Later, much later, their crews had eaten. Some had even slept!

This was another day. The rain had ceased and the moisture was being sucked up visibly from the sodden earth, making progress that morning more likely than had been anticipated at sunset. Even so, Lavanski had limited his advance. Dawn found his troop seeking a wide ditch and wallowing into hull-down positions to wait there until the battle situation had been clarified by the reconnaissance units swanning to the north-east, and also by Patton's HQ which was now operating with the main body of the US 3rd Army, to the north-west.

At five am, a full company of US Rangers joined the troop and despatched foot reconnaissance patrols pending orders to push on with the advance.

The infantrymen came back half an hour later with reports that the ground ahead was clear of Germans. They'd climbed the slopes to the north and scanned the surrounding countryside through binoculars. They'd also used hearing devices, but there was no indication of enemy presence. It seemed evident that what remnants of the SS 4th Panzer Army had managed to withdraw from the concerted American frontal attacks were hell-bent on making the Sarthe river crossing before the routes could be sealed.

The reaction of 5th Armoured Divisional HQ to this Intelligence was immediate and their ensuing orders clear and concise: sharpen the angle of the spearhead and proceed directly towards Beaumont-sur-Sarthe. Reinforcements in strength already mobile.

Lieutenant Richard Bannen, commanding No 2 Squadron, rushed forward in his Jeep the three miles to Lavanski's laager, where he summoned an orders group of troop commanders. There they orientated their maps to the ground and, on the talc covers, chinagraphed the route they would take regardless of the weight of German opposition.

'Steam-roller the bastards!' Bannen shouted over his shoulder as he stalked back to his Jeep. 'I guess it's up to us to give "Ole Blood an' Guts" a surprise for a change!'

Even so, right now he wasn't ambitious enough to commit his squadron without an infantry screen. The Krauts were just bloody-minded enough to have laid an ambush of PAK-41s along that trail through the valley. The US Rangers would move ahead in strength – and on foot!

Sturmann Klaus Stumm got his MG-42 section to their feet and they moved off in the same formation, but switching to a more northerly course. If they bumped into the Yanks, then they'd have to adjust their route again. And, if the worst came to the worst, the section was small enough and sufficiently well-equipped to lie low for two or three days. It would be bloody stupid to risk charging hell for leather into an American ambush. They would fight, all right! Bloody hard, too! But only if they'd more than a fifty per cent chance of coming out on top. Now it was mid-morning and they pressed on with the sun coming up high.

Kreutzmann was looking ill and his breathing had become laboured, but he didn't complain and Stumm, marching at his side, paid him little attention, senses alert to the sounds of war crowding in on all sides. Here in the forest they were at least safe from air attack. All they had to do to survive was make sure they spotted any enemy patrols before the Yanks spotted them.

Out in front, Scherfe and Kleiser had widened the angle to a distance of more than fifty metres between them. Both had their eyes slitted against the dazzling sun, trying to use the rims of their steel helmets as visors as they probed the treetops and matted undergrowth ahead, as wary of snipers as of hidden Browning machine guns.

They had been marching for the best part of two hours when Kleiser halted, rifle raised high in his right hand in the regulation halt signal. Stumm joined him to find the big man looking down into a depression in the woodland, a bowl of lush greenery in which nestled a farmstead with outbuildings forming the three sides of a square. In the meadows surrounding it, cattle and horses were grazing contentedly.

To one side, parked neatly in the shade against the wall of the house, stood an American Willys armoured car. It had a great white star painted across the full width of its bonnet and a red and white pennant fluttered from its radio antenna. On the tailgate was the insignia of the US 5th Armoured Division. Its turret hatch was open and the single-barrelled Browning clipped to its rim was tipped skywards.

Across the farmyard stood a 30cwt truck with the same insignia, also deserted.

Stumm signalled Kreutzmann and Scherfe and the two came to join him at the double, using the tall trees as cover, taking no chances. Then, as a section, the four of them moved farther down the hillside where Stumm set up the MG-42 machine gun between the trunks of two trees, using the roots as a firm base for the bipod legs. He tested the range of traverse and made motions for Kreutzmann to clip in an ammunition belt. Then he cocked the first round into the chamber and ordered Scherfe farther still down the hill to a point overlooking a gully to the right. Finally he sent Kleiser back up the slope in a makeshift semblance of all-round defence.

They sat back in the long grass, sipping red wine from their water bottles; Kreutzmann feeling all the better for the enforced rest, Stumm impatient to spring his ambush.

Time passed and the sun grew hotter. Eventually, sounds came from the house. French voices, men's and women's. American voices loud with alcohol.

A thin smile touched Stumm's lips and he turned his head to Kreutzmann, who nodded his personal agreement to the sturmann's unspoken words — green Yanks!

People came out from the house. There were five American soldiers including a bare-headed sergeant, three Frenchmen and two women. The women were all over the Americans, obviously revelling in their sudden and unexpected liberation. For them the war was over. After five endless years, at least they could begin to live again!

Minutes passed, but the Americans seemed in no hurry to move off. Stumm kept the butt of his MG-42 to his shoulder, an eye to the sights, a forefinger at first-pressure on the trigger. Then, as the section waited, came the familiar prrt . . . prrt . . . prrt and the people in the farmyard crumpled silently to the ground.

Kreutzmann hooked an arm beneath the gun, scooping

away empty cartridge cases. There was no point in Stumm
shooting again. The series of short bursts which had taken
almost the full length of the ammunition belt had been
devastatingly accurate.

The section remained in position, watching for movement
amongst the corpses. Maybe some were shamming death.
There could also be more people in the house. More civilians.
A full minute passed. Two. Three. Then Stumm called to
Kleiser and Scherfe.

'Right, you two! See what still moves!'

Stumm and Kreutzmann watched the lumbering Kleiser
and the rangy Scherfe weave their way the half-kilometre to
the farmyard. They halted warily at the boundary wall, contemplating the house and the few outbuildings in their three-
sided square. They were talking urgently together, and
occasionally one of them pointed at the pile of bleeding bodies
huddled over the centre drain. They were obviously thinking
that the MG-42's sudden burst could have alerted other
American patrols.

Stumm continued to watch, blank-faced. He was asking
himself just how much of the fire-and-movement drill he'd
taught them they'd remember now they were out on a limb. But
then, sure enough, Scherfe huddled himself behind the wall and
levelled his Schmeiser across the top whilst Kleiser crossed the
cobbles to the bodies. He looked down at them dispassionately
and unhurriedly fired three shots at point-blank range into the
pile. Then he signalled to Scherfe, who left his cover position
behind the wall and strode over to join the big man.

Stumm unclipped the ammunition belt from the MG-42 and
stood up, propping the machine gun over his shoulder and
heading for the farmyard. Kreutzmann followed a few yards
behind him, still pale, but feeling better for the rest. He was
thinking thank Christ they'd found themselves some transport.
His first reaction had been to take the armoured car, but on
reflection he realised that Stumm had been wise in insisting on
the 30cwt truck. An armoured car in the congestion around
the Sarthe river could cause problems.

As Stumm reached the bodies, young Scherfe came out of
the farmhouse. His machine pistol was slung with his rifle over
his shoulder and his arms were laden with liver sausage and an
assortment of bottles.

'There's more food than we'll need, Sturmann!' he shouted
as he headed for the truck, at which Stumm sent Kleiser for
more whilst he and Kreutzmann began collecting the weapons

44

from the dead Americans. It would be bloody stupid to leave them lying around for the French Resistance to get their hands on! He also picked a couple of American helmets and a greatcoat from the armoured car, which he handed to Kreutzmann.

'The other two can go up front,' he decided. 'We'll rig up the Spandau under the tilt.'

Kleiser appeared with a wooden box piled high with food and bottles of wine and cognac, which he shoved between the canvas flaps of the tilt above the tailgate. Then both he and Scherfe swapped their steel helmets for the American 'flower-pots' which Stumm had collected. Scherfe climbed behind the wheel. Kleiser went round to the front passenger seat and settled himself down with his Schmeiser on his knees.

'Now we head due west,' Stumm told Scherfe. 'If we bump into any Yank infantry it doesn't matter a bugger. Keep the side windows up. That'll stop the bastards chatting an' they won't see much through the reflection. We'll be watching out from the back, here.'

'We could do with a road map, Sturmann . . .'

'Get moving!'

The engine fired at the first tug at the starter and Scherfe let in the clutch, circling the pile of corpses towards the lane which led from the farm. He looked down on them thinking they looked contended under the bright sun. If it hadn't been for their blood welling over the cobbles, he could have believed they were sleeping, even in such grotesque positions. One of the women was very young, probably not more than sixteen or seventeen, and she was lying on her back a short distance from the rest of them with her dark eyes wide open and her rich brown hair spreading behind her head like a pillow. Pity about her, he thought. The battle had been too sudden and too one-sided. None of them had had a chance, for Stumm's shooting had been faultless. Hell of a thing for these American boys to end their lives as pointlessly as this!

It was as they neared the farm gate that a sudden shriek behind them caused Scherfe to stamp on the brakes. He spun round to see a plumpish woman wearing a black dress and a headscarf dashing from the house.

She yelled, '*Arrêtez! Mes camarades. Arrêtez!*'

Under the canvas tilt, Kreutzmann was lining up his Schmeiser, a round in the breach, but as he took aim she tore away her headscarf. Kreutzmann paused. Her head had been cropped so that all that remained was a thick dark stubble.

'Wait! Please wait!' she called breathlessly, holding up what appeared to be a photograph.

'Sturmann?' Scherfe was poised with one foot on the brake and the other hovering over the accelerator, seeking orders.

'Hold it!' Stumm said and Scherfe slipped the gear into neutral and hauled on the handbrake.

The woman held out the photograph to Stumm.

'See! See, Herr Sturmann! This is my *mann*! See! He is a hauptsturmführer with the 17th Panzer Division. SS! I can prove it. I also have letters! I was with him for over two years. Please take me with you!'

Stumm looked at the photograph.

'Where is he now, this hauptsturmführer of yours?'

She shook her head and spread out her hands.

'I do not know! He left when the war got close. Perhaps he may come back for me. He said he would try, but the Resistance is everywhere. Now they are hunting for collaborators.'

'Then you were lucky!'

He pointed to her shaved head, but she shook it emphatically.

'That's not all,' she told him and turned round to slip her dress from her shoulders, baring a criss-cross pattern of angry weals still oozing blood. She pointed to the pile of bodies in the centre of the yard and spat in their direction. 'This was only a start,' she told Stumm. 'They were holding me for the Resistance.'

'Can you shoot a gun?'

She shrugged, shaking her head.

'I have done no fighting, Sturmann, but I will fight for my freedom. Give me a gun and I will show you!'

Stumm looked contemplatively at Kreutzmann, who shrugged his indifference. An extra gun in an extra hand, no matter how inexperienced, could make a lot of difference in a tight corner. Stumm turned back to the woman, his mind made up.

'Climb in!' he told her, 'and keep out of sight. You'll find some Yank Walthers there. They take our 9mm ammo . . .'

She was having difficulty climbing over the tailgate and her skirts got hooked on one of the tilt-fastening cleats.

She looked nightmarish with the sun glinting off her shaven head.

The section motored out of the farm gate feeling easier in mind.

After the dicey start to a day in which the French farmer could just as easily have been an American patrol, this decisive battle here at the farm had come as a boost to their morale. They had also come to realise that whilst the main force of the Wehrmacht 7th Army was withdrawing in some disorder to the Sarthe river, there were still delaying tactics which could be employed, even in guerilla roles. The US 3rd Army, despite the speed of its advance from the Cherbourg peninsula, was going to have no easy run through to the Sarthe – particularly once the 4th Panzer Army had dug in along the east bank.

Scherfe clung to the minor roads, navigating by the sun in an effort to maintain a general north-easterly direction, heading for the town of Sable and the main bridge there over the river. He guessed it was unlikely to have escaped the US heavy bomber raids, but the defenders would already have thrown pontoons across or erected a prefabricated bridge.

Presently, they began to pass through villages in which people were lining the narrow streets in their hundreds. Some were waving tricolours, some in tears, others offering bottles of wine to Kleiser and Scherfe in the front seats – a clear indication that other American lorried infantry had recently passed that way. But the Germans acknowledged these wild greetings with little more than the casual lift of a hand, keeping the side windows closed as Stumm had ordered, knowing that these happy villagers would quickly turn into killers if they suspected these were panzergrenadiers.

Scherfe maintained a steady fifty kilometres an hour, taking the bends at speed heedless of what might lie beyond, accepting their commitment. Even so, it had become apparent that the American spearhead, which had swung to the south-east of the main Wehrmacht concentrations, had widened a deep salient in their defences and it was going to be a matter of luck which army reached the major crossing points in strength first.

It was as they topped the range of hills west of Cornay that Scherfe spotted an American motorised column winding its way across the valley some six kilometres ahead. He braked heavily on reflex and that caused Kleiser to jerk forward and crash his steel helmet against the dash. Obscenities also followed from the back of the truck where the MG-42 had overturned on top of Stumm and Kreutzmann.

'What the hell is it?'

Scherfe spun round to find himself looking into Stumm's face. The sturmann had his Luger in one hand and there was aggression as well as anger in his pale blue eyes.

Scherfe jabbed a forefinger ahead.

'American motor column, Sturmann! See, down there in the valley? At about six kilometres!'

'Then tail on to the bastards! Move it!'

Scherfe's mouth dropped open.

'It's a Yank column, Sturmann!'

'Do you think I'm blind? I believe it's even sunk into Kleiser's thick skull that we're behind the enemy lines! All right! So catch it up you stupid sod! How do you expect to reach the Sarthe? Fly over their bloody heads? We'll ditch the truck when I say the time's right! You got that?'

Scherfe shot a quick glance at Kleiser, slumped in the passenger seat with only the narrow slits of his eyes indicating that the man wasn't asleep. He turned back to Stumm and nodded.

'Very good, Sturmann! Like you say! We'll tail on to the Yanks!'

'I also said, let's move it!'

Scherfe breathed again as Stumm slid behind the canvas tilt to realign the MG-42 through the centre flap. It was clear to Scherfe that if the Americans tumbled to who was aboard this truck then Stumm and his old buddy, Kreutzmann, planned to get out the back way and to hell with everybody else! He wondered if Kleiser had been bright enough to have worked that out for himself.

It took them twenty minutes to catch up with the American column and, as they drew closer, they found it was not one of lorried infantry as they'd suspected, but a supply column of some kind — stores, ammunition. Deployed at intervals along its length were a half-dozen and more half-tracked vehicles mounting anti-aircraft guns.

Scherfe passed this information to Stumm, who made no comment, but Scherfe himself felt some relief in the knowledge that he wouldn't be compelled to stare into the faces of American soldiers lining the tailboard of the truck in front. But they'd not been closed with the column more than a few minutes when additional trucks appeared from a side road and moved into position behind them. This was a massive convoy and it was impossible to estimate its length. All they knew was that they now had Yank vehicles in front and behind. There was no way out.

More French villages and more civilians lining the streets, cheering and passing wine to their American liberators. At one hamlet they came upon an armed band of thirty or forty

Resistance fighters raising their weapons in salute and the Americans tossed them packs of Camel cigarettes as they swept past — another clear indication that things didn't look good for the withdrawing Wehrmacht.

It was as the column reached the eastern limit of the valley and began to weave its way into the woodland beyond that there came the sudden wail of sirens from the command vehicles midway down the convoy. A warning immediately repeated along its length.

Scherfe caught his breath.

Luftwaffe!

It had to be. What else?

Christ! And how they'd prayed for the support of just one squadron during the one-sided infantry battles of the previous day!

Ahead, the Yank trucks were deploying from the road to a pre-determined drill and more than half had made it under cover by the time the first German fighter-bomber swooped into its strafing attack.

'Junkers Ju-88s!'

Scherfe yelled over his shoulder to Stumm as he swung the wheel wildly, the rear wheels skidding and slithering over the loose earth. There was no mistaking the Luftwaffe's 'schnellbomber' with its protruding twin radial engines and perspex nose. With a range of close on 2,500 kilometres and the speed of a fighter these could have come from anywhere in Western Europe. Trouble was they were twenty-four hours too late! And, as the truck accelerated into the undergrowth, Scherfe lifted his eyes to glimpse a formation of ten aircraft breaking into attacking sections, the first already committed to its dive.

He shouted his warning into the back of the truck whilst Kleiser snatched up his Schmeiser and clipped on a magazine.

'Stupid bugger!' Scherfe yelled at him.

But as he spoke the offside rear wheel dropped a full half-metre into an irrigation ditch. There followed a fierce wrenching, tearing, sound. The truck lurched violently and then tipped sedately on to its side.

Scherfe found himself sprawling on top of Kleiser's fat body, stabbing blindly with his boots for the dashboard, seeking sufficient leverage to reach and throw open the door.

He scrambled out as the first stick of bombs straddled the head of the convoy and, even at that distance, the blast of the explosions struck his face. He rolled over the front wheel, screwed sideways and still spinning, then dropped to the ground to find Stumm, Kreutzmann and the Frenchwoman scrambling from beneath the canvas tilt. Stumm dragged out the MG-42 and angrily led them from the wrecked truck, seeking both cover and a defensive position in the ditch. Scherfe eyed him speculatively as more bombs dropped, closer now, considering whether the sturmann intended taking up the war again from the ground once the Junkers Ju-88s had completed their bombing runs. By this time, Kleiser had also struggled clear of the truck and he ambled towards the ditch without a glance in Scherfe's direction. Only when he saw Stumm and Kreutzmann setting up the MG-42 on its bipod did he notice that they were wearing their Wehrmacht helmets.

In and amongst the quickening blast of HE bombs there now came the measured thump-thump-thump of medium anti-aircraft guns. Evidently, the American half-tracks were already engaging; but the roar of aircraft overhead indicated that the initial strafing runs had been completed. At that very moment four Junkers Ju-88s screeched above at a speed which made it barely possible to identify the black crosses on their fuselages and wings. Seconds later, they were climbing steeply and banking in wide circles for their second run.

Scherfe again glanced across the shallow ditch towards his section leader and the sturmann stared back at him with an expression which indicated neither reaction to the section's predicament, nor anger that the Luftwaffe should arrive too late and only after a decisive battle had been fought and lost. Could be, Scherfe told himself, the sturmann was happy that a hell of a lot of American soldiers were about to die – which was enough to think about right now! When the Junkers Ju-88s turned for home would be when he'd find the time to look at his own personal involvement.

The second section of Ju-88s dived into strafing attacks, selecting targets farther along the column, seeking maximum casualties. They were also using cannon and machine guns as they pulled out of their bombing dives, and splinters of bark were being torn from the higher branches of the trees and floating down sedately on to the crouching, huddled Americans.

There came screams. The frantic, agonised screams of mortally-wounded men as the casualties began to mount. Deep furrows suddenly erupted in the soft ground alongside the irrigation ditch and more screaming carried from across the track some fifty metres distant. Stumm lifted his face from the earth, peering from beneath the rim of his steel helmet, to see the bomb-blast tossing shattered American bodies high into the trees. Disintegrated limbs dropped from the branches; torsos, draining blood, which appeared to hesitate as they became entangled amongst the lower foliage before dropping silently into the undergrowth. More American screams! Many at the sheer horror of the carnage they were witnessing even before their first blooding in battle.

Seconds later, the third wave of Junkers Ju-88s struck the column following the sortie's strafing pattern and, as Stumm's MG-42 machine gun section stared skywards from the irrigation ditch, they watched the bombs detach from the underside of the aircraft, unerringly aimed by the velocity and angle of the dive. And, at the point when the Ju-88s momentarily levelled, so the full firepower of their cannon and machine guns hit the Americans, even before the bombs had landed.

Then the first stick exploded and fountains of earth mushroomed, tossing bodies into the undergrowth where they lay still, mutilated and oozing blood.

A few minutes later the Ju-88s had gone, their second runs completed. Most of the screaming had ceased and an awesome silence hung over what remained of the US transport column.

Klaus Stumm cradled the MG-42 in his arms and began to squirm out of the ditch, keeping himself flat to the ground, whilst Kreutzmann motioned to Kleiser and Scherfe to follow. It was clear that the column had reached its final resting place. All the Americans could do now was count their dead and give what help they could to their wounded. And, from the panzergrenadiers' point of view, it would be stupid hanging around any longer!

Some of the Americans were beginning to stir, with wary calls from one truck crew to the next.

Kreutzmann glanced down at the Frenchwoman retching in the bottom of the ditch and when she shrank from his hand he kicked her viciously in the stomach and thrust the barrel of his Schmeiser within inches of her face.

'Either you come now or you die,' he said quietly. At this she nodded hysterically, but crawled out of the ditch in much the same way as Stumm had done, heading for the thicker woodland where a litter of dismembered American corpses lay.

Here the grass and undergrowth was sticky with their blood. There were lumps of flesh and entrails, raw and still oozing blood, scattered like a carpet across the ground. On the spiked cone of a holly bush the head of a fair-haired boy was poised as it had tumbled from the trees. Incredibly, the face was unmarked and even the blood from the severed neck had dripped neatly into the ground leaving the tree still fresh and crisply green.

It was as Stumm's section got to within a few metres of the trees that there came a sudden wild cry from the road.

'Sarge! Krauts, godammit! For Christ's sake look at the bastards!'

The section flattened themselves to the ground, instinctively turning to face the threat as a Browning machine gun opened up at a range of less than a hundred metres, the bullets singing high into the trees, toppling the head of the fair-haired boy.

Stumm lowered the bipod of the MG-42 whilst Kreutzmann slithered through the grass with a loaded ammunition belt in his arms. When he got close enough, he tossed one end of it to Stumm who clipped it into the breach and cocked the weapon. The US Browning was still firing spasmodically, combing the area where the panzergrenadiers had been spotted, and was soon joined by a second machine gun from farther down the convoy.

Scherfe, who was closest to the wood, guessed that if he were to live through this action then his only hope was to make a run for it. But as he braced his legs Kreutzmann hurled a smoke grenade which burst a good thirty metres away. Immediately, as the white smoke began to cascade, there came more shouting from the Americans and the intensity of their gunfire increased. In reply Stumm fired a short burst from the MG-42. As the seconds turned into minutes it became apparent to the Germans that no American service corps soldier was going to risk charging through that smoke into the jabbering muzzle of the Spandau. They'd taken a helluva beating from the Luftwaffe and their convoy had been wiped out even before they'd sighted their forward infantry. There was no point in piling up more casualties by being bloody stupid! What did a few odd Krauts matter now, anyway?

As the Browning continued to rake the woods, Stumm motioned to his section. He unclipped the ammunition belt and tossed it back to Kreutzmann to reload. Then, along with the Frenchwoman, the four men moved silently into the tall trees.

Chapter Four

Extract from a personal letter from Lt Colonel Wendell Needham, commanding No 1 Battle Reconnaissance Group (Operating with 2nd Free French Armoured Division spearheading US 3rd Army Northern Sector – ultimate objective, Paris) to Lt General George Smith Patten, GOC, US 3rd Army.

'During the whole of the day American armoured and infantry patrols have tested the strength of the withdrawing German 84th Corps. Against every rearguard defensive position of panzers and panzergrenadiers the Group has initiated aggressive artillery, mortar and armoured attacks. Whenever possible these have been supported by strafing fighters, fighter-bombers and heavy bombers of the US Army Air Force. Under this continued pressure, the German 84th Corps is beginning to give way and the sector astride the town of Villedieu held by the German 353rd Division has been penetrated. Units of my command are already pouring through the gap with the objective of encircling the German 116th Panzer Group.'

At the same time, American Headquarter Units and tank commanders in the field latching on to German radio communications intercepted positive enemy reports to the effect that Oberkommando Wehrmacht had accepted that the German military situation in Normandy was rapidly deteriorating and that the fighting could no longer be confined to the Cotentin Peninsula around the allied bridgeheads. OKW also admitted that the US 3rd Army had begun a wide enveloping sweep which could threaten the whole of the German military machine in Northern France. Furthermore, the morale of the *frontline troops was beginning to flag under the ever-increasing weight of American fire power and armoured pressure. Desertions had already been reported – even amongst crack panzer and airborne formations ...*

Obersturmfuhrer Hans Thielker, commanding the battle-weary remnants of the 2nd Battalion of the 4th Panzergrenadier Regiment of the 12th SS Panzer Division, Hitler Youth, made a final tour of the defensive positions prior to dusk stand-to. In all, he had thirty-three men left under his command, which included two rottenfuhrer section leaders and one unterscharfuhrer. Ten of the grenadiers were seriously wounded and would already have been transferred to a forward field dressing station – had there been one.

Now the detachment was dug-in in an all-round defence location at the corner of a wood which overlooked the main road towards L'Aigle – two MG-42 light machine guns, one 5cm Granatwerfer 26 infantry mortar and one 7·92mm Granatbuchse infantry anti-tank rifle. The three NCOs carried MP-40 Schmeiser machine pistols, the rest of the grenadiers G-41 (M) self-loading rifles. But ammunition was short and probing patrols, sent forward during the late afternoon, had come back with reports that American armour supported by lorried infantry had already bypassed their positions and were advancing at speed north-west against little opposition.

To Obersturmfuhrer Hans Thielker and his men the situation was becoming desperate; but since the early months around the Normandy bridgeheads they had learned to accept casualties. During July, in the first big push by the British 30 Corps, the Wehrmacht had suffered over fourteen thousand casualties and received little more than two thousand reinforcements. This weakening drain on manpower had subsequently increased during unrelieved months of commitment to front-line battle. Similarly, ammunition, petrol and stores had diminished but, true to tradition, the 12th SS Panzer Division Hitler Youth had fought with a tenacity and determination which had earned the grudging respect of the Allies, as well as that of their own GOC Oberfuhrer Kurt 'Panzer' Meyer.

Thielker's plan was to remain under cover and preserve what remained of his troops and ammunition until he could either tag on to some other withdrawing Wehrmacht formation or collect sufficient stragglers to form a strike-force capable of breaking through the American flank. Such a manoeuvre would not only open up a path towards the main body of the Wehrmacht, withdrawing systematically to prepared defensive positions to the east, but might retard the advance of the US 3rd Army sufficiently long for counter-attacks to be launched against reconnaisance and armoured formations racing for the Dives and Sarthe rivers.

It was a sound plan and Hans Thielker, twenty-five-years-old and a graduate of the Leipzig Military Academy, was determined to see it through as best he could. Somehow, this slow but positive erosion of the 2nd Battalion had to be arrested and morale boosted even amongst his battered survivors.

As dusk silhouetted the tops of the tall pines against a luminous evening sky, Thielker took off his steel helmet and wandered from foxhole to foxhole, chatting impersonally with the men standing-to their weapons. He would also check on the ranges they had calculated, study the approaches to dead ground through binoculars, saving a cheering word for the more badly wounded who, ashen-faced and bleeding, respon-ded by making little of their injuries.

With stand-down he went back to his HQ position in the centre of the all-round defensive circle, squatting on the edge of his slit-trench, staring down at the sturdy body of Paul Muller, his signaller and wireless operator. As ever, Muller was scanning the operational wavelengths with earphones clamped beneath his helmet. He looked up and shook his head at Thielker's unspoken question. Silence. Nothing but silence. The Wehrmacht had evidently cut all radio communication. Only the US 3rd Army crowded the ether.

With the onset of darkness the noise of battle some kilometres to the east intensified. The steep slopes of woodland were pinpricked by muzzle-flashes of medium and self-propelled artillery whilst, still farther to the east, the orange blasts of high explosive indicated where some Wehrmacht battle group was still attempting to maintain a defensive line.

Thielker calculated that the fighting must be between eight and ten kilometres distant. In turn, that caused him to consider whether or not he should hang on to his positions at the edge of the wood regardless of their domination of the road in daylight. Time wasn't on his side! The wounded were an additional problem and he had doubts whether any of them were capable of marching that distance.

The matter was still chasing around in his mind when there came a sharp challenge, from deeper within the wood.

Unhurriedly, Thielker jerked a round into the breach of his MP-40 Schmeiser machine pistol.

'Sir!'

He recognised the voice of Unterscharfuhrer Heinz Boeckh.

'Yes?' Irritably. 'What is it?'

'A machine gun section, sir! A sturmann with three men carrying weapons and ammunition . . .' he paused, then . . . 'there's also a Frenchwoman with them!'

Sturmann Klaus Stumm hadn't expected to bump into SS positions on the southern slopes of that wood. The fierce challenge hurled from the darkness had brought him up short.

'Friends!'

He had shouted and pushed himself forward rather than risk Kleiser, in his ignorance, or Scherfe, in his inexperience, bring down a fusilade of small-arms fire. Now, whether he liked it or not, he had to play along.

He motioned Kreutzmann and the woman to tag behind him and for Kleiser and Scherfe to bring up the rear. Things could have been worse he told himself as they moved forward – the bastards could have been Yanks!

Even in the half-light, Stumm recognised the uniform and death's head insignia of an unterscharfuhrer of the 12th SS Panzer Division Hitler Youth and he made a show of bringing himself to attention, holding the MG-42 by its flash eliminator in much the same way as he would have held a rifle.

He reported, 'Sturmann Klaus Stumm of the 3rd Panzergrenadier Company, 9th Division, with three men and a French *collaborateuse*!' He swung his head to indicate those behind him.

Boeckh nodded, relieved.

'Good!' he said at once. 'We can use an MG-42 team.'

But then his eyes narrowed as they focused more closely on the tall, rangy figure of Stumm, running them over the lean dishevelled face with its three days' growth of curling fair beard; the bleached, stained uniform; the intensity of the blue eyes beneath the rim of the coal-scuttle helmet. He turned to survey the rest of the section. The dark man who was either ill or badly wounded; the heavily-built farmer's boy whose helmet was perched incongruously on top of his great head; and the soldier who was little more than a boy, but with a

56

strange wildness already tensing his young face.

To Boeckh the development no longer looked good. These men looked too independently operational, with the machine gun belts slung about their necks and the leather straps of their equipment slotted with stick grenades.

Besides, there was this Frenchwoman . . . !

Impulsively, he jabbed a finger in her direction.

'Who's she?'

Stumm shook his head.

'Never asked her name! She did us a good turn and she's handy with a gun. That's all that matters, isn't it?'

The unterscharfuhrer still looked doubtful, but eventually he nodded. 'Maybe. You'd better come and meet the obersturm-fuhrer.'

'What outfit is this?'

'Twelfth. Second Battalion. Fourth Panzergrenadiers. Or what's left of it!'

Stumm pulled a face which brought an immediate reaction.

'What the hell you grinning at, Sturmann?'

But Stumm's expression didn't change. He held out his right arm which showed the change in texture of the material of his tunic sleeve where the Grossdeutschland cuff insignia had been.

'Maybe we've all seen better days,' he said.

Obersturmfuhrer Hans Thielker didn't have the doubts which Unterscharfuhrer Heinz Boeckh had reflected towards the newcomers and he greeted Stumm and his MG-42 machine gun team as an answer to a prayer. He led them to the south-eastern perimeter of his all-round defensive system with orders to dig in with their arcs of fire concentrated on the road below. Stumm saluted and the section unbuckled their entrenching tools and got down to work, whilst the sturmann pored over the range charts which the riflemen men had already prepared.

Later, the four of them and the woman squatted in the coarse grass at the edge of the wood, where they turned out their haversacks and ate the remainder of the food, washed down with the red wine which they had taken from the farm by the escarpment. All the same, they'd have preferred the liver sausage and the cognac they'd had to jettison with the American truck, and they cursed the Yanks for their aggression after the Junkers Ju-88 raid.

Afterwards, Stumm took the Frenchwoman deeper into the trees, where she bared her breasts and lifted her skirts for him. He sank into her, telling himself that a fat and willing woman like this one was worth a hundred squalling bitches like the one Kleiser had killed at the farm. Rape only had its place with a victorious advancing army. An army on the run provoked derision, even from the women as they were being raped – and that could do nothing at all for a man, no matter how long it had been since he'd last had a woman!

He took her a second time, then a third, leaving her where she slept noisily flat on her back with her heavy legs still wide. She could be anybody's now – he still didn't know her bloody name!

During the early hours there came renewed activity from the slopes to the east, but there was no movement along the road in the valley and the SS detachments operating on a two-hours-on and a two-hours-off rota managed to get some sleep.

After dawn stand-to, Thielker decided to continue north-east through the wood in an attempt to bypass the area of the night's battle. He had told his men in a few crisp sentences that it didn't matter a damn any more whether they encountered Wehrmacht or American forces first. If they were American, then it might be possible to launch an attack against their flank and take some pressure off the defenders.

Kreutzmann turned to grin at Stumm at such logic, aware that the obersturmfuhrer evidently had not considered the possibility of Wehrmacht counterattacks in strength – just went to show how the possibility of ultimate defeat could creep insidiously into the minds of even the most dedicated SS commanders!

An hour later the detachment reached the north-eastern tip of the wood, and as the main body closed with the two forward riflemen scouts they saw a stretch of open meadow and the huddled buildings of a small railway halt astride a single track about a kilometre away.

Thielker came forward, a frown deepening across his forehead as he scanned the panorama through binoculars.

'Robichon!' he told Boeckh. 'I can read the name on the platform. Check it out on the map!'

Boeckh dragged a large-scale map from beneath its talc cover and traced the route of their advance through the forest with a stubby forefinger.

'Robichon-sur-Florentin, Obersturmfuhrer,' he confirmed. 'There's a village two kilometres to the south. Church with a spire marked!'

Thielker handed him the binoculars.

'I see no movement at the halt!'

Boeckh adjusted the lenses and swept the binoculars from left to right over the tiny railway station and the narrow cobbled road which evidently led to the distant village. Then he focused on the lean-to sheds on the platform, on the signal box with its short flight of wooden steps and on the two huts which housed tools and permanent way equipment.

Eventually he lowered the binoculars and turned to the officer, shaking his head. 'No movement, sir!'

Thielker wasted no time and swung round to his section commanders.

'Forward machine gun sections out on to the flanks! Move!' Then, 'Rottenfuhrer Zimmermann! Take two men and make a quick recce of the halt. Use the hedgerows. You've got cover and we'll put down smoke if need be. Right? Move!'

From his section's new position amongst the tall grasses on the left flank of the formation, Stumm watched the rifle section led by Zimmermann, carrying an MP-40 Schmeiser machine pistol, move warily in single file from the woods to the hedgerow, making a wide flanking movement which would take them to the road which led from the halt to the village.

He jerked a round into the breach of the MG-42 without taking his eyes from the action developing in front of him, ready and alert to open fire at the first hint of an ambush – American or French Resistance. To the right, in the gap between his section and the next, the detachment's wounded were grouped, most of them with limbs swathed in blood-stained and begrimed bandages. There was one man with a leg severed below the knee, the makeshift tourniquet of field dressings and rifle pull-throughs still dripping bright red blood into the green undergrowth. He then glanced at Kreutzmann who was holding the ammunition belt steady and jerked a thumb over his shoulder at the wounded man. Kreutzmann nodded with a grim smile, his own pain easing at the sight of the same kind of selflessness which had been the inspiration of the Grossdeutschland Division on the Russian Front.

Zimmermann's group had reached the road into the village and he had established his riflemen in defensive positions along the hedge which gave them adequate fields of fire into the station buildings. Then he motioned two men forward. They moved off rapidly in crouching positions with their rifles and bayonets thrust out in front of them.

'All right, men! Now we follow up!'

This was Thielker, who had got to his feet and was pointing to where the reconnaissance section had gone to ground. Then,

'Sturmann Stumm! Lead your section ahead. HQ follows. Rottenfuhrer Eiser! Your MG section brings up the rear. The wounded stay put and ready to give supporting fire. The woman stays, too! The rest . . . move!'

Stumm's section slung the loaded machine gun belts about their necks and set off at a steady jog to join Zimmermann in the hedgerow, knowing that Thielker's positive leadership was doing a lot for their morale. They moved quickly with the knowledge that a man-to-man battle with Yank infantry could be imminent — and that would be their chance to show the Americans they bloody well weren't going to have everything their way!

A few minutes later the main body of the detachment closed with the point rifle section, which was still giving cover to the two forward scouts who were doubling back from the halt.

They halted breathless.

'They're all dead, Rottenfuhrer!' one of them gasped with a strange wildness about his eyes. 'All the train load. They're dead! Women, children, the lot!'

Zimmermann stared at them, from one to the other, with incredulity in his eyes. 'Are you saying the Americans did that?'

The private soldier shook his head emphatically. 'The Americans haven't been here. It was the Waffen SS! There's a couple of 'em lying crushed on the track. The Waffen SS chopped up the whole train load!'

'How many?'

The soldier shrugged. 'They're lying everywhere. Maybe a hundred of 'em. All dead!'

By this time Hans Thielker and his runner had reached the forward section.

'And the Waffen SS, Dorkmann? Are they still at the halt?'

The soldier turned swiftly to the officer, shaking his head. 'There's nobody there but dead French civilians, Herr Obersturmfuhrer, and the two Waffen SS men crushed by the train.'

Thielker turned to look across the narrow road to the forward MG-42 section and caught the eyes of Klaus Stumm, considering whether or not to commit them to whatever threats might lurk beyond the narrow gully of the railway track, for there was something about these half-crazed-looking men who had come from the darkness to join his detachment which jarred on his nerves. There was more than a hint of the fighting animal in their eyes and in the lines deeply engraved into the faces of even the younger pair. It was also significant that Unterscharfuhrer Boeckh, who was a stickler for discipline in the line of battle, hadn't ordered them to clean up. But when he turned back to the halt he thrust the impulse from him. Stumm and his men would have the chance to prove themselves soon enough. There was nothing to be achieved by sacrificing his firepower.

He turned to bellow over his shoulder. 'Detachment will advance in deployed sections! Rottenfuhrer Eiser! Lead on with your rifle group and two scouts forward at fifty metres!'

'One Section prepare to move!' Eiser echoed. 'Follow me! Move!'

They climbed on to the narrow gauge railway line, advancing at an easy pace towards the raised platform, rifles held high at the port, eyes anxiously scanning the trees which looped overhead to form a green arch further down the track. Ahead, one of the forward scouts raised his rifle in an all-clear signal.

The section continued at the same steady pace, coming upon the white painted signal box on the opposite side of the track to the platform. An attempt had obviously been made to start a fire, for there came the acrid stench of burnt timber. Inside the hut bodies were heaped into an untidy pile. Blood had dried crustily upon them, naked limbs blackened by the heat of the makeshift fire. There was the corpse of a young woman sprawled across the entrance. In death she still held a baby to her breast. Half its head had been axed away and the mother just lay there with her long black hair heavy with congealed blood.

Inside, it became apparent that the Waffen SS had piled kindling wood and bales of straw on top of more bodies, but these had not burned either. Farther along, a woman lay face down in the grass beside the track, her legs riddled with machine gun bullets, her hands severed at the wrists as though she had made some last futile attempt to plead for her life. But her skull had been smashed into her brain and her two hands, one with its wedding ring, lay in little pools of blood at her knees.

The rifle section moved on towards the platform and its lean-to buildings, where there were still eddies of black smoke curling lazily into the bright sky. Here was the stench of scorched human flesh, as appetising to the soldiers' taut and empty stomachs as had been the bodies of their comrades, seared by US napalm during the bloody battles of forty-eight hours earlier. To the lumbering Kleiser it did no more than remind him of the pre-marketing slaughter at the farm where he had laboured in Oestrich-Rheingau. And it caused young Rudi Scherfe to realise that despite the wanton killing and maiming of the past months there could still be new horrors to shock a man's senses.

Obersturmfuhrer Hans Thielker stalked to the head of the column, joining the point rifle section and looking neither to right nor left. Then he halted abruptly before the bodies of the two German soldiers wearing the dark green uniforms and insignia of the Waffen SS. One was lying face down between the rails, but the other had been run over by the train and his torso had been almost severed at the waist. The wheels had dragged his intestines along the track as it had pulled away. They appeared startlingly white against the texture of the brown stone ballast.

'Rottenfuhrer!' Thielker turned to Eiser. 'Cut off the insignia and give it to me. Check on their paybooks and dog-tags. Quick as you can!'

The last order came of its own volition as Eiser withdrew his fighting knife and bent over the German corpses. But immediately the officer realised why he'd suddenly sensed a need for urgency. There was something about this silent railway halt which had nothing at all to do with his kind of war. Why the massacre? he asked himself. What had caused this detachment of the Waffen SS to go stark, raving mad? Who had given the order for the mass killing? And why had they suddenly needed that train so badly? The French people had obviously been casual agricultural labourers making the journey to help with harvest at the village to the south — Robichon-sur-Florentin.

Could this be the work of some mutinous band of deserters, gathered together from the ragtags of demoralised Wehrmacht units, to whom killing had become a way of life and who were now wreaking their anger and disillusionment on any hapless French civilians who happened to stray across their paths — innocent men, women and children?

Thielker didn't know and he would never know. Again he found himself staring into the mocking face of Klaus Stumm, whose luminous blue eyes told him clearly that the man had been reading his thoughts. Stumm had been aware of the dangers in getting mixed up in this kind of carnage long before he had!

'Unterscharfuhrer Boeckh!' Thielker bellowed. 'We move out . . .' He paused momentarily to glance at the map which hung in its talc cover from a strap about his neck. 'We move north through the trees across country.'

Boeckh hurried to the head of the column to march beside the officer, evidently seeking some comment on the massacre, but at that moment Eiser joined them to hand Thielker the insignia he had cut from the uniforms of the dead Waffen SS men. These the officer stuffed into an ammunition pouch and said nothing.

The detachment progressed up the hillside in extended order, widely spaced sections in single file in a broad 'V' formation, weapons at the ready, machine guns slung on their broad webbing straps from the necks of the gunners. From this point, each and every copse could conceal an ambush.

The men on the right flank of the formation could still look down upon the railway track where, from one of the lean-to buildings, there protruded the half-burned body of a young boy. There were bayonet punctures through his narrow chest which had speared the body to the wooden platform on which he lay. His throat had been slashed and the blood had congealed into the hair and dripped down the steps in a black, glutinous paste. One leg was twisted at the knee as though it had been jammed intentionally into the half-open door.

In a colourful spread of garden alongside the track lay two women and a small girl. The child, still clutching a blood-stained doll in one hand, lay face down amongst a vermilion mass of flowers whilst one of the women had an arm extended towards her as though, even in her death throes, she had made an attempt to protect her. The other woman was some distance away. She had been beaten about the head with an axe which lay at her side, her hands and wrists shredded as she had tried to ward off the blows.

When he saw an undulating spread of meadowland directly ahead, Rudi Scherfe breathed a great sigh of relief. And, seconds later, they marched past the Robichon-sur-Florentin village limits where the sign, freshly painted, leaned drunkenly against the hedgerow.

A kilometre farther along the detachment halted to consolidate with the wounded, moving systematically into an all-round defence formation. At the rear, Klaus Stumm unobtrusively set up his MG-42 machine gun pointing back along the route they had taken from the railway halt.

The band of wounded looked a pitiful sight as they plodded wearily into the centre of the circle, one step being forced visibly after another. Faces death-white and haggard with pain. Filthy field dressings wound amateurishly about wounds which had called for a surgeon's knife days, even weeks, ago. Helmets scuffed and bulged by flying shrapnel.

But to Obersturmfuhrer Hans Thielker this was no time to rest.

'Rottenfuhrer Eiser! Your section will take over the point! Keep moving!'

The panzergrenadiers stared at him wanly as they shambled past and, despite the shade of their coal-scuttle helmets, Thielker could see they had reacted to the tableau of death at the railway halt. His lips twisted in a wry smile at the knowledge that to those of his men who had followed him so far, that wasn't their kind of war either.

The Frenchwoman brought up the end of the straggling line of wounded, supported by one of the men who had difficulty in standing upright himself. Thielker could see she was close to collapse and there were streaks of vomit down the front of her black dress. Her face was deathly pale and her eyes rolled as she faltered on the point of fainting. But then she recognised Klaus Stumm and his MG-42 section. She made a brave effort to straighten her back and detached herself from the wounded grenadier, to stumble across the grass and flop to the ground where Stumm's section were dismantling the machine gun and on the point of moving off. Stumm didn't even look at her, and as he slung the MG-42 over his shoulder she somehow managed to climb back to her feet and stagger after him.

An hour passed during which the sun rose high and the temperature soared. Men frequently dropped in silent heaps and the NCOs left them where they lay, for fitter men at the rear of the column to revive with water and red wine.

Eventually, they came upon more wooded country and all breathed sighs of relief at the prospect of shelter from the beating sun and the dank moisture which would rise from the soft earth left by the storms of the past few days.

Several hundred metres into the trees, Thielker again called a halt and the panzergrenadiers sank amongst the ferns and couch grass to wolf down whatever rations they'd been able to preserve in their haversacks. Then they sprawled on their backs, staring into the dappled blue sky through the foliage of the tall trees, feeling the sweat dry cold on their bodies and sharing their last cigarettes.

Half an hour later they got stiffly to their feet, discovering new pains in their over-taxed muscles. Many of the wounded turned to Thielker, silently pleading for more rest; but he reacted roughly, himself setting a pace ahead of the wounded with Unterscharfuhrer Heinz Boeckh crowding them from behind. Only when the column had begun to maintain a reasonable speed were they redeployed into a tactical formation.

They came upon a man-made clearing amongst the trees, some four hundred metres long and up to a kilometre in width. Thielker immediately spread his rifle sections wider, the fit men moving to the flanks along with the MG-42 sections; the wounded forming an all-round defence in the centre.

Long-experienced, the panzergrenadiers instinctively moved into their battle positions, and when the first mortar bomb exploded twenty metres to their rear none of them reacted, but maintained the axis of advance towards the next belt of woodland now a couple of hundred metres ahead.

There followed a salvo of mortar bombs, more accurate now, and two of the wounded crumpled silently into the grass. Unterscharfuhrer Boeckh, still with the rear rifle section and three men of the HQ detachment, dropped still farther back and had them set up the 5cm Granatwerfer 26 infantry mortar. They used the detachment's last three smoke bombs on a range which positioned the short barrel almost vertical in the soft earth. But, as Boeckh had known they would, the bombs dropped neatly across the line of trees ahead, cascading thick white smoke.

Immediately, as they burst, Browning machine gun fire began to rake the open space on the chance of picking up random casualties.

Kreutzmann pulled a face at Stumm.

'Two of the bastards!'

Stumm nodded.

'That's all. Two!'

So the Yank ambush was a small affair, probably some lone infantry platoon swanning loose as part of a battalion reconnaissance.

Kreutzmann was still watching Stumm.

'Are we playing, Klaus?'

Stumm pointed to the smoke from the Granatwerfer, now drifting within a few metres of the advance rifle section.

Stumm's blue eyes glinted.

'You gone bloody stupid or something?' he shouted back. 'We'll let this lot thicken an' then slide off to a flank. Let that silly bugger Thielker win the war on his own, if that's what he wants. Right?'

He glanced to the rear where Kleiser and Scherfe were

P.—C

closing up. They had obviously heard and when they caught his eye they both nodded readily, as eager to avoid the kind of sacrificial battle looming ahead as Kreutzmann had been. This might well be only a Yank infantry platoon making a bloody nuisance of itself, but right behind it was the whole of the US 3rd Army. The Sturmann was right. Wherever he was to lead them would be better than dying in this bloody great God-forsaken forest where they could bleed to death and rot in the open.

Farther back, the Frenchwoman was gamely stumbling after them. She'd made an effort to shove the horrors of the Robichon halt to the back of her mind and was hanging on to the Germans only because there was nothing else she could do. Besides, she wanted to put as much distance as possible between herself and the scene of the massacre. She reckoned that if it came to the crunch, and this battered panzergrenadier detachment happened to be captured by the Americans, she could always claim that it was they who'd done the killing and buy herself a passage to safety.

So she hung on, and when the American riflemen began to add their firepower to the Brownings she, along with Stumm's section, slid through the smoke into dense woodland to the far left of Thielker's line of advance. They crashed through bracken and the low branches of trees, heedless of the noise they were making and secure in the knowledge that there wasn't a chance in hell of them being pursued. Thielker's soldiers would have their hands full without having to take time off to round up deserters.

This had been a good time to get out, too! Thielker would never know whether they'd run for it, or whether they'd become casualties in pushing home the attack.

It was over an hour later, when the trees began to thin again, that Stumm halted to search the ground ahead through binoculars.

He handed them to Kreutzmann.

'Take a look, Franz,' he said quietly. 'What d'you make out over there?'

Kreutzmann examined the ground ahead in much the same way as Stumm had done. A couple of minutes elapsed before he dropped the binoculars. Then he turned to Stumm. 'Defence post? Strong point?' he suggested. 'But thank Christ one of ours! Maybe some panzer laager and re-fuelling depot.'

'Is it still manned?'

Kreutzmann grinned at that. 'You know as well as me that

the Tiger crews are always pretty smart when it comes to camouflage, Klaus!'

'Yeh! That's what I had in mind . . .'

Stumm turned towards the heavy form of Helmut Kleiser, who had squatted on the ground with his broad back propped against a tree trunk, considering whether he should detail the man forward to reconnoitre. If Kleiser happened to bump into a Panzer VI Tiger squadron it was a certainty they wouldn't let him loose again. But that didn't matter a damn, did it? Kleiser was expendable, anyway, and as far as Stumm was concerned the sooner the fat bastard dropped from the section the happier he'd be!

Kleiser looked up, sensing the sturmann's eyes on him, hostility building up at the prospect of again being used as a dummy to stick out his neck into whatever lay ahead. His narrow eyes hardened and a hand closed of its own volition over the butt of his Schmeiser machine pistol. He knew that Stumm hated his guts, but he wasn't going to let the mad bastard send him to his death. If need be, he'd gun the man down!

But Stumm had changed his mind.

'We'll go round!' he decided. 'We move back into the forest and arc north-east.' He turned to the Frenchwoman. 'You! Bitch!' He spat the words at her. 'You get yourself to the front, right?' He pointed ahead to a narrow footpath which skirted the perimeter of the wood at that point for a distance of some two hundred metres. 'Move!'

But the woman hesitated despite his aggression, face pale and body tense. 'Me? Why me?'

'Because we take it in turns, that's why!' he snarled. 'If you want you can piss off right now. Is that what you want? Is it? Then do as you're bloody told! Lead on down the track there.'

Still she hesitated, her mind unable to assimilate Stumm's reasoning. She shot a questioning glance at Kreutzmann, but he met her unspoken query with the kind of aggression in his face he'd shown her during the Luftwaffe's bombing of the American supply column. And that threw her mind back to the more recent massacre at the railway halt and she turned along the footpath with head bent, the heaving of her sobs breaking the silence of the woodland.

Scherfe was about to follow her but Kreutzmann caught his arm, shaking his head.

They let her get some fifty metres ahead before Stumm signalled Kleiser to follow, at which the big man pushed himself to his feet and plodded after her. More distance, then Scherfe followed, and behind him Kreutzmann and Stumm close together with their eyes fixed on the woman ahead.

So the section moved within the perimeter of the wood, the Frenchwoman being allowed to maintain her lead and Kleiser being angrily called back whenever he tended to close the gap. They spotted the gable end of a house deeper in the wood, but there was no sign of life there. That meant little. Chances were it could be manned by either Americans or French Resistance and this was no time for Germans to stick their necks out. Trouble would come soon enough!

Now they were moving into the thinner woodland they'd spotted a quarter of an hour earlier. Here the trees were not so tall and the undergrowth was sparser, too. Dead ground! Kreutzmann was thinking the crews at the panzerlaager could have done something about the change in terrain . . . and when the mine went up with a flat and flashless explosion it was obvious why Stumm had sent the Frenchwoman ahead to blaze the trail.

Breathing heavily, pouring sweat and knowing nothing of ground-level trip-wires, she saw a small metal canister the size of a jam-jar suddenly leap out of the ground a couple of metres in front of her. For a fleeting second she stared transfixed, as though it were some strange animal suddenly dislodged from its burrow.

Then the canister burst.

The case shattered under the detonation of the explosive charge and the ball-bearing shrapnel scattered faster than the speed of bullets, twenty or more fragments striking her stomach simultaneously. Their force hurled her backwards, but a tree trunk stopped her falling and she stared down at her belly with disbelief, to see what remained of her intestines suddenly bulge from a bubbling mass of red porridge to overflow down her legs and pile like so much mixed-up spaghetti about her feet.

With eyes bursting with panic and horror she stooped, vainly scooping at her intestines, slimy with blood and mucus, with both hands, gathering them together and trying to shove them back into the gaping hole in her stomach.

She spun round wildly to face the Germans behind her. Now *she* knew why they'd sent her alone along this footpath. The bastards had suspected that it must be mined somewhere.

'Bastards! Boches bastards!'

She screamed at them, surprised that she could still make a

sound. But then the pain hit her and the pitch of her scream heightened. Her arms were losing their strength and she was no longer able to hold on to the tree trunk. Yet, she knew she must not fall on to her stomach or she'd never get those things back inside.

Somehow, despite her agony, she managed to twist herself on to her back and she lay in the undergrowth with her blood pumping over her breasts and thighs.

Farther back, Stumm was shouting something to Helmut Kleiser and raising his Luger automatic. Seconds passed before Kleiser grasped what Stumm had in mind, but then the big man hurried down the footpath to the screaming woman and shot her through the head. It struck him that he was getting into the habit of murdering women. They came easier than Americans, anyway!

Chapter Five

Beyond the mined path, Stumm took over the point of the section, setting a good pace and heading due east; not so anxious about bumping into American patrols as he was to put as much distance as he could between the section and Thielker's panzergrenadiers.

South of Trenville the topography was changing. No longer were there woods draping the undulating Normandy countryside. Here the ground was flat and mainly arable, with long straight roads bordered on either side by ancient elms and poplars.

Whilst there wasn't the density of cover for a roaming band of soldiers, neither was there the danger of an ambush at every forest fire-break.

Only Franz Kreutzmann was reacting badly to the increased pace, but he voiced no complaint, appreciating the necessity of Stumm's action. Yet he had difficulty in maintaining position and detailed Rudi Scherfe to bring up the rear. In his weakened state, Kreutzmann was beginning to have difficulty recalling the chain of events which had occurred since Stumm had broken away from the main body of the 3rd Panzergrenadier Company after the big battle with the US armoured division. The incidents between had barely registered in his mind. But it didn't matter, he told himself. They were all part of this same war and nothing would ever change, really. The bombing, the shelling, the hand-to-hand fighting and the killing would go on forever. Each day would bring more and more enemy reinforcements. It didn't matter a damn whether they were Russians, Americans, British or French. They would come to the front day after day after day after day — and so on to eternity. That's how it was to be and nothing could change it for any of them — but death!

Death!

He never really thought about it — apart from times like this when he became irrational with pain and exhaustion. But death could always be an easy way out. A sudden mushroom of orange flame in the undergrowth, the dull thud of an explosion, a burning, weakening pain – or not even that – and then a sweet oblivion. And the war would go on just the same without him. Millions of other soldiers would march and fight themselves into the dregs of exhaustion – just like he was now, but the important thing for him was that he wouldn't be amongst them!

Why was it Klaus Stumm never felt like this? he asked himself. Why was it that Stumm could march all day and all night with an MG-42 machine gun slung over his shoulder and a couple of loaded ammunition belts slung around his neck and never falter? Kreutzmann grimaced. Maybe it was because the man was the Devil himself. The blue eyes set deep above the curling blond beard rarely reflected anything other than venom. A soldier without a soul. A soldier who wanted nothing more than the freedom to go on killing the enemy soldiers who strayed across the sights of his MG-42.

Only when the war frizzled into nothing and when Germany had at last been beaten to her knees would Klaus Stumm also shrink into a disillusioned husk of a man whose mind would, by that time, probably be incapable of recalling the atrocities he had witnessed as well as those he had himself committed.

Kreutzmann unclipped the water bottle from its canvas sling and poured a little of what remained of the red wine into the palm of his hand. This he splashed on to his brow, letting it run over his eyelids and cheeks. He slid the chin-strap free and eased the steel helmet from his head, finding more relief in the cooling breeze which filtered through his sweat-matted hair.

His legs had become leaden, his muscles so taut they might snap with the next step he took. The chances were that he'd never make it as far as the Sarthe river. But Stumm would. That was for certain. Maybe that ignorant, lumbering bastard Kleiser would too; for he was bloody stupid and lucky enough to walk through a Yank barrage without knowing it – and come out unscathed at the other end.

But how about young Rudi Scherfe, marching stolidly behind him and carrying more than his share of ammunition? Would he make it? Maybe not. The lad was really still a schoolboy, and like all German schoolboys who'd suddenly found themselves at the fighting front he'd reacted well. But that didn't mean he'd get by! Not so, poor little sod! Sooner or later, his inexperience would let a bullet through between his eyes or a Yank bayonet into his belly. That was the way things went and there were few exceptions.

Kreutzmann began to lose more ground and made an effort

71

to close the gap between himself and Kleiser.

But, at that moment, Stumm halted and yelled back for Scherfe to join him at the point.

Lieutenant Roger Bailey of the 2nd Infantry Battalion of the US 5th Armoured Division sprinted a dozen metres up the hillside to watch his forward foot patrol deploy as it warily left the cover of the trees. Only an hour earlier they had debussed from light personnel carriers in the headquarters' laager of the 2nd Armoured Regiment and the air of uncertainty which hung over these as yet unblooded troops was very apparent.

'OK, you guys!' Bailey bawled down to them from his high position. 'Let's speed it up outa this goddam valley!'

Corporal Vic Sullivan, leading Number One Section at the point turned to look up at the officer, grinning.

'Maybe we shouldn't be down here at all, Lootenant!' he commented, jabbing the muzzle of his Thompson sub-machine gun in the direction of the copse on top of the hill. 'Could be them woods are thick with the Krauts!'

Bailey didn't answer, but it was a thought which had crossed his own mind. Brigade Intelligence reports had indicated that odd detachments of German SS formations were fighting their way back east in a race for the Sarthe crossing points. There had also been reports of armed bands of deserters which had been killing, raping and looting their way into the hills south of Trenville.

But what the hell? This had nothing to do with him! His brief had been to seek Intelligence on skirmishing German battle groups; operational groups, both infantry and armoured, which could constitute a threat to the pencil-thin lines of communication between the American forward elements and their main armoured concentrations.

'Sullivan!' he yelled back. 'Maybe you're right! We'll take a peek at the woods. Follow the line of the hedge to your section's right. Platoon Headquarters follows. Then Two and Three Sections. All right? Lead on, Corporal!'

Sullivan was still grinning as he beckoned over his shoulder, 'Follow me, One Section!'

And he ambled off with the chin-strap of his helmet hanging loose over his epaulette and his Thompson sub-machine gun slung carelessly over his right shoulder. The seven riflemen followed by the Browning machine gun section of three brought up the rear in single file.

Sullivan glanced nervously behind him.

'Space it out you guys, what the hell!' he yelled and there followed some shuffling amongst the section until they had opened up about a couple of metres between men. In this manner they began to climb the long slope towards the belt of trees which topped the rise, each with his eyes pinned on the dark tunnels of foliage which led into the woodland beyond.

As the gradient steepened they began to sweat and blow under the weight of their equipment, but what worried most of them — and that included the NCOs — was what they were expected to do if, as Vic Sullivan had joked, the woods did happen to be crowded with German infantry.

For this was the first time that the 2nd Infantry Battalion had taken over the point of the divisional flank-guard. More than that, it was also the first time they were being committed to direct contact with the Wehrmacht. This, to most of the platoon, had been a hell of a long time happening but, on the other hand, the entire US 3rd Army hadn't been let out of its reserve role until 'Ike' Eisenhower had issued them with swanning orders and detailed 'Ole Blood an' Guts' General George Patton to hook south-east behind the main battle zones of the British 2nd Army and race for Paris and the wide open country to the east.

That had been less than two weeks ago.

Now, here and for the first time, there was likely to be every chance of putting to the test the endless routine of field exercises they'd been practising over the English South Downs during the past eighteen months. It wasn't going to be too difficult, either, for reconnaissance reports and the speed of the US main armoured spearheads towards the Sarthe river had proved that the Wehrmacht was all washed up, anyway. It was going to be no more than a matter of mopping up the few pockets of resistance still holding out on the flanks.

All the same, they recalled long periods of battle drill when everybody had used blanks and there had always been a hot meal waiting for them at the end of the day. There was to be no more of that, they told themselves. Besides, fighting in woodland could be as nerve-racking and every bit as dangerous as street fighting, and they'd had an eyeful of that as they'd passed through Argentan on their way to link up with their forward armour and personnel carriers.

In this kind of summer weather blood ran thinly, and the streets of the town had run red with it. Corpses, in contrast white-faced and haggard, had sprawled along the roadside and at street corners, looking as though vampires had swooped and

73

wasted no time in gorging their fill. This had been a brutal introduction to the wanton killing and maiming of modern warfare and many of the platoon had reacted by vomiting into the fresh blood at their feet.

But here, in the warm French countryside, the fighting would be cleaner. Here they would have time to concentrate on staying alive.

With about two hundred metres to go to the copse, Sullivan halted his section and they sank down in the long grass, sweat streaming down their faces, the sensation of prickly heat uncomfortable under arms and crotch. But they looked at each other placidly enough, finding some relief in knowing they'd got so far without raising a squad of German mortars. Some of them pulled out cigarette packs, but there were others who were unwilling to let their eyes stray far from the forward line of the copse.

Lieutenant Roger Bailey pushed forward his Platoon Head-quarters with his runner, Private Mario Vergetto, and flopped down in the grass beside Sullivan, binoculars at the ready. This, too, was Bailey's first experience as a point-platoon commander and he was confidently determined to cope with whatever might lie ahead. He eased back his helmet from his close-cropped head and put the binoculars to his eyes.

Minutes passed. Then he turned to Sullivan, shaking his head and causing drops of perspiration to fly from his forehead.

'Not a goddamn thing,' he announced.

Sullivan shrugged, then pointing to a spread of open ground a hundred metres short of the copse. .

The officer pulled a face. He knew that unless the entire platoon could be launched on a full kilometre flanking movement there was little chance at all of avoiding that hundred and fifty metre wide stretch of open ground.

He tugged at his lower lip pensively, thinking that maybe this was the first decision of any importance he'd been called upon to make since he'd disembarked from the LST on to the Mulberry jetty.

Piddling little decision, anyway!

He turned back to the corporal.

'Take your section forward. Vic,' he told him, quietly. 'See the dip in front of the line of gorse just short of the edge of that open patch? Right! Space out an' make for that. We'll cover you an' then join you up there. OK?'

Sullivan clipped home the loose end of his chin-strap and

slid the tommy-gun from his shoulder. He shoved the safety catch forward and jerked a ·45 round into the breach.

'Sure, Lootenant!' he agreed readily, then turned to his section. 'You guys heard that? We tail off to the first line o' gorse up there. Prepare to move, One Section!' There came the sound of more scuffling amongst the infantrymen, of bolts jerking rounds into rifle chambers, of bayonets being clipped home, the heavy metallic clank of machine gun ammunition belts.

Bailey flopped over on to his back, propping himself up on his elbows in the long grass, scowling down the hillside into the sun where his other two sections were grouped.

'Right fellers!' he called down to them. 'One Section's about to move up. Keep your eyes an' weapons pinned on that copse just in case something erupts up there!' Then, back to Sullivan, 'Right, One Section, move!'

He watched the section get awkwardly to its feet. He was thinking there wasn't the kind of urgency about their movements which a dicey situation like this demanded. The idle buggers looked all the world as though they were still on those damned exercises where there'd be a couple of brass hat umpires waiting over the brow of the hill.

Sullivan must have sensed it too.

'Move it, goddamn you!' he bawled across the open ground to his Browning team at the extreme right of the formation. 'This isn't a bloody holiday!'

Lance-Corporal Ben Jackson, carrying the Browning, grinned cheerfully back at his section leader and waved an acknowledgement. Then the three of them increased their pace until they drew level with Sullivan's riflemen.

It was whilst they still had fifty or so metres to go to their first bound that there came the sudden, staccato prrt ... prrt ... prrt ... of an MG-42 machine gun. With it, the four men at the tail of Sullivan's rifle section crumpled unprotestingly into the grass.

The rest of the section hit the ground as one man and Private Jimmy Gorso, who had seen his mate suddenly throw up blood, began squirming over the ground to where he lay writhing.

But Sullivan's voice pulled him up short.

'Leave 'em, goddammit! This is no time for first-aid. Look to your front, Gorso! An' that goes for everybody else!'

Lower down the slope, Lieutenant Roger Bailey spun round to his other two sections. 'Anybody see the muzzle flashes? Anybody see anything move?'

But there came nothing but stunned silence from the men. In a split second they'd seen four of their buddies die or, at least, be seriously wounded. Four buddies who'd sailed with them from New Jersey over two years back had gone in that same split second! Jesus Christ! Their pale expressions asked, What's this all about?

'Anybody see anything?' Bailey shouted again. 'Christ! Didn't I tell you to keep your eyes fixed on that goddamn wood? Corporal Standish! Corporal Minzetti! Did none of your men see anything move?'

Still nobody answered and when he stared along the line of faces he saw only that the two section leaders were shaking their heads, whilst most of the men still had their eyes focused on the bodies of the four men who had become casualties. And, at the same time, a voice deep inside him was telling him that if there could be one Kraut MG-42 in that copse, then there could be a dozen, and here was his green platoon stuck out in the open on the goddamn hillside with only a rookie officer to help them survive.

He settled himself deeper in the long grass, flat on his stomach with his binoculars again to his eyes. The worst had happened. The fears which had tormented his sleep ever since he'd set foot in Normandy had materialised into reality without warning. Here he was, commanding an unblooded platoon, facing an enemy strongpoint and the truth was that all he wanted to do was crawl back down the hillside and into the oblivion of the 5th Armoured Division's advance.

He recalled the training manual on infantry tactics which had been drilled into his class at the Officers' Training College way back in Portland, Maine . . . "if it has not been possible to pinpoint enemy defensive fire during the opening phases of the attack, then sacrifices must be made in the movement of forward troops with the intention of inviting more enemy fire. Only when the siting of enemy weapons has been established is it possible to develop the attack."

Again he scanned the edge of the copse.

Still nothing! Not a goddamn thing!

This looked like being the day when he made his own personal down-payment for all the good times he'd had in England with his string of Limey women! There always had to be a day of reckoning and here was his — right now!

'Corporal Sullivan!'

Sullivan, lying flat on his belly with his head just raised sufficiently to keep the copse in his line of vision, lifted it a few inches higher to glance over his shoulder at his platoon commander farther down the hill.

'Sir!'

'Move your machine gun section fifty metres to the right!'

Sullivan stared at him, not moving.

Then, 'But we're being observed! We're under fire!'

Bailey came back at him angrily.

'You know the drill, Corporal! Cover them with your rifle section. Now move it, for Chrissake. Move it!'

Sullivan shrugged and turned to his right where Lance Corporal Ben Jackson had the Browning machine gun sited on its bipod. Numbers Two and Three on the gun, still with their rifles slung over their shoulders, were laying out loaded ammunition belts.

'You heard that, Ben?' he called across the distance. 'Move the gun fifty metres to your right. OK? We'll cover the copse!'

Jackson gave him a long wry look and wiped some of the sweat from his eyes before he gathered up the heavy weapon in his arms. He was telling himself that he wasn't going to get all that much covering fire with four of Sullivan's riflemen already dead or wounded. All the same, when the two men had looped the ammunition belts round their necks he jumped to his feet with spirit.

'Follow me, fellers!' he called and they got up from the grass as quickly as he had done.

Lower down the slope. Bailey held his breath with eyes glued to his binoculars, sweeping along the line of the copse and back again, seeking that tell-tale orange flash from somewhere amongst the undergrowth.

But there was nothing. No sudden, vicious squirt of accurately aimed 7·92mm Spandau bullets. No staccato bark of the instantly-recognisable, rapid-firing MG-42.

Platoon Sergeant Abel Kalowski moved up from the tail of the rear section to join his platoon commander. He was a big man, a regular soldier who'd made his name on the regimental drill squares of Portland, Maine. But he was as green to active service as the rest of this platoon. All the same, he was quick to put two and two together.

'The bastards are playing with us, sir!'

Bailey nodded.

The German machine gunner had deliberately withheld his fire. Now Bailey had one section forward and the Browning section out on a limb a further fifty metres to the flank. He'd already lost the spearhead of his attack!

'Corporal Sullivan!'

Sullivan turned again with anger suffusing his dark cheeks. He was on the point of asking if there was only one goddamn section in this platoon. But Bailey went on, 'Two Section is to move forward to that fold in the ground before the open patch. Prepare to give covering fire and for Christ's sake keep your eyes open for that Spandau!'

Instant relief flooded Sullivan's face.

'Roger! Stand by One Section!'

Bailey turned to Corporal Bill Standish.

'Prepare to move, Two Section . . .'

Standish interrupted him.

'We've got smoke with the mortar!' he shouted. 'Wouldn't it be better to put down smoke, first?'

'What the hell for?' Bailey came back at him angrily. 'What the hell are we supposed to do about that bloody Spandau if we can't see it for smoke? You heard, Corporal! Prepare your section to move. Now! Move!'

Warily, Two Section scrambled to their feet, crouching low, the rifle section under Standish moving farther out to the right flank, the Browning machine gun section advancing directly up the slope.

They moved methodically over the thick grass, hugging the hillside, weapons pushed out in front of them, using what cover and fire-and-movement drill they could with first the rifle section and then the Browning section advancing in bounds. Faces were tense and fingers tight on triggers, but they moved deliberately up the hillside and closer to the shallow dip before the stretch of open ground.

Bailey watched their progress tight-lipped, ready to call down covering fire at the first flash of the German machine gun in the copse. But the MG-42 still didn't fire and as Two Section dropped into position he breathed a great sigh.

He glanced across at Sergeant Kalowski, who shrugged his massive shoulders in an unspoken "so what now?" question. Bailey ignored the gesture and ran his eyes over One Section's Browning group way over on the right flank.

'Lance Corporal Jackson!'

'Sir!' Ben Jackson's acknowledgement came back loud and strong.

'How much of that copse are you covering with the Browning?'

'Top o' the trees! That's all, I guess. An' the steeper we elevate, the sharper the angle . . .'

'OK OK! Then prepare to give it a five second burst. Stand-by! Fire!'

The chatter of the Browning so close at hand hit the platoon and to a man they raised themselves on their elbows and craned their necks. All they saw was a few branches suddenly snap from the tops of the trees and come floating down to earth.

When Bailey looked back at Kalowski there was a new expression on the officer's face, a new glint to his eye.

'You want to know something, Sergeant?' he asked. 'Something real important?'

Kalowski stared back at him with that same tolerant good-humoured smile about his lips, and it was clear to Bailey that the man's confidence in the command hadn't risen any during the last few minutes.

'Sure, sir.' Kalowski then replied easily. 'You tell me!'

Bailey squirmed over the grass back to the location of his Platoon Headquarters. He yelled to the boy with the R/T set who had established himself at the far left of the group, with the long antenna reaching over the grass and waving in the breeze.

'Faggio!'

The R/T operator looked up from his set. He had discarded his helmet and he lifted one of the earphones clear of his dark curly head as the officer addressed him.

'Lootenant?'

'Have we contact yet?'

Faggio shook his head. 'Guess not, sir! Too much heavy stuff around right now. There's a helluva tank battle on the band, though. Maybe five kilometres east!'

'OK! OK! Let me know as soon as you make contact!'

Bailey began to make his way back to his previous position behind Standish's Number Two Section, but after a few yards he halted with a new thought buffeting through his mind. Could be that the Krauts weren't all that smart after all, he reflected. Maybe they weren't playing some mad game with what they recognised as a platoon of greenhorns. Maybe the bastards only had one gun up there! Just one bloody Spandau!

He'd been on the point of telling Kalowski that he was about to risk a frontal attack on the copse anyway, but now things had changed. He raised himself sufficiently high on his elbows to see both his forward sections.

'Now listen, you guys!' he shouted at the top of his voice. 'I guess we've been farting about just long enough on this hillside! Down behind us is the whole of the Second Battalion an' we're going to make damn sure they don't come breathing down our necks. You all got that?' He paused, looking over his section in turn before continuing, 'So we're going to put in an attack. An attack! An' this is how I plan we'll do it. Now! It could be that the Krauts up there can speak English. Well, if they can that's too bad I reckon, for they'll know what to expect, but it's a chance we gotta take. Also, I'll tell you that I got me a hunch that there's only one Kraut machine gun up there an', more than that, it's getting low on ammunition. That's why the bastards have been cagey on showing us just where they're lying low. OK! So it's a hunch! But it's a chance we gotta take!'

Again he looked over his deployed sections and he found that most of the men had their heads turned his way. He was on the point of yelling at them to face their fronts; but he stopped himself, realising that it would be smarter to let them concentrate their minds on the coming assault.

He raised his head still higher, knowing he was taking a chance with any sharpshooters there might be up in the copse, but it was also a show of nonchalance which had to be seen and recognised as such by his own men.

His voice became crisper, 'This is how we're going to do it, fellers! Objective! To eliminate or capture enemy machine gun position in copse directly ahead. Method! Left flanking! Numbers One and Two Sections will remain in their present positions to give covering fire. Each section will fire machine guns into copse in bursts of five seconds duration alternately and at three-minute intervals. Sergeant Kalowski will be in command of fire-control!'

Momentarily, Bailey turned to the burly platoon sergeant. 'You got that, Sergeant?' he asked, at which Kalowski grinned and nodded, relieved that he wasn't to lead the assault section.

'OK!' Bailey went on. 'Meanwhile I shall be taking Corporal Minzetti's Number Three Section, together with Platoon Headquarters' mortar section, back down the hill an' round the spur from where we'll climb back into the woods about three hundred yards short of that copse. I reckon it should take us a good quarter of an hour to get round there. At the first clearing we come to in the wood the mortar section will set up a position and be prepared to blast the enemy with high-explosive. My signal will be a red Very flare! You all got that? A red Very flare! So keep your eyes skinned for it in Numbers One and Two Sections, for on that same flare I want both sections to give thirty seconds' rapid fire into that copse. That means riflemen as well as Brownings! When your fire cuts, I'll lead Corporal Minzetti's section into a bayonet and tommy-gun assault against the flank of the Kraut strongpoint. After the attack, the platoon will consolidate in that goddamn copse!'

He paused, seeing the two forward sections were already snuggling down into fire positions. To the rear and at the bottom of the hill the men of Three Section were looking anxiously at Minzetti who didn't appear to be too sure of himself. The words 'bayonet assault' had had a blanching effect on the raw troops. But Bailey kept the zip high in his voice, 'OK. Any questions? Corporal Sullivan?'

'No questions, sir!'

'Corporal Standish?'

'None, sir!'

'Sergeant Kalowski?'

'No, sir!'

'Right! Sergeant, you start the first burst of fire with One Section and in exactly two minutes from now!'

'Roger!'

Bailey called to his three-man mortar team.

'Lance-Corporal Evans! Follow me and bring with you as many HE bombs as you can carry!'

And with that he slid down the hill on his backside, getting to his feet as soon as the gradient became sufficiently steep to shelter him from the German machine gun.

'OK, Tony!' he said to Minzetti as he joined the waiting Number Three Section. 'Let's not waste time. Lead your section on behind me in single file!'

Up in the copse, Sturmann Klaus Stumm stared speculatively over the rim of the hill into the blue sky and hazy countryside beyond. What he couldn't see was the platoon of American infantry which had deployed across the patch of dead ground a hundred metres below. But he knew they were there and the raucous voice of the man who was more than likely their officer had given him a fair impression that something was going to blow up – and soon!

Stumm wished he was able to understand English – as much as Lieutenant Roger Bailey had prayed he couldn't! As it was, he'd have to check the options open to the Yanks, and bloody quickly!

This wasn't a situation which Stumm had sought. With Thielker's private war probably still raging to the south-west and the dangers surrounding the massacre at the Robichon halt still farther west, Stumm had only been intent on making as much headway as possible in the other direction. But the terrain had been difficult and the worsening condition of Franz Kreutzmann had compelled him to rest-up. The American patrol had caught him unawares and he'd ordered his section to lie low on the off-chance that they'd skirt the base of the hill and take to the easier lower ground to the north-west. But that bloody officer had shown he'd either got a military mind or he was damned stupid. Probably stupid, Stumm reconsidered. If he'd been bright, then he wouldn't be in command of such green troops.

Their initial blustering approach on to their position had forced Stumm to give them a short burst from the MG-42 and he knew that he'd chopped down half a rifle section. But if he hadn't, then the Yanks would have blundered straight into the copse and neither he nor his section were in any condition for hand-to-hand fighting against a full infantry platoon – no matter how green they were!

So now he was stuck with it! There'd been moments when Stumm had thought that their indecisive officer might take an easy way out of a situation he was unsure of handling and sheer off to a flank. But the man had had a surge of conscience which had decided him to make a fight of it.

Stumm had moved the MG-42, mounted only on its bipod, to the very edge of the copse, providing an arc of fire which covered the rim of the hill and spanned a full hundred and eighty degrees.

About fifteen metres to his left was Rudi Scherfe with rifle and MP-40 machine pistol, covering the ground which dipped below Stumm's angle of vision and where he knew the machine gun team of one of the Yank sections to be positioned.

Facing the rear and completing the panzergrenadier all-round defence pattern, the huge body of Helmut Kleiser lay some thirty metres distant on the westward-facing edge of the copse.

Stumm recognised that the four of them were too thin on the ground to resist a spirited attack by the Americans, but it would be equally suicidal to attempt a withdrawal until they had shown their hand. In the heat and flurry of a dog-fight there was a far better chance of them sneaking back along the road they had taken.

Either way, this was a situation which had to be faced for it was obvious that the Yanks didn't intend to go away.

So now Stumm was squatting relaxed behind his machine

gun; the butt resting on his thighs, his last cigarette smouldering between his thin lips.

Next to him, an ammunition belt already clipped into the breach and five more stacked neatly beside him, Franz Kreutzmann had identical thoughts running through his head. But Kreutzmann also had other worries. Though this was by no means the first time that Stumm and he had waited patiently for an assault to be thrown at them, knowing they were to be outnumbered by enemy soldiers and overwhelmed by their firepower, it was the first time Kreutzmann had been practically incapable of movement. The searing pains which had cut across his chest during the last few kilometres of the march had not cleared up with rest. And the weakening breathlessness which accompanied them convinced him that all the pain didn't stem from his old shrapnel wound. The rigours of the past five years, and the body-destroying privations of the Russian Front over two winters, had done to him what they had done to so many other panzergrenadiers they had left dead in copses identical to this one.

The trouble was that the strength of a man's body wasn't up to the degree of his commitment. No way was he going to be able to continue Stumm's march; but even after their years together he still hesitated to tell him. He guessed that Stumm would do no more than scowl at him from those hard blue eyes of his and probably not even trouble to comment. More likely than not, the sturmann would throw a couple of ammunition belts around his own neck and move away as though he hadn't spoken. That would be Stumm's way of saying that the war had to go on!

Rudi Scherfe was also apprehensive about the section's predicament. Could be that Kleiser, half-asleep and puffing at a cigarette, didn't have a care in the world, but to Scherfe it was apparent that the sturmann had made a wrong decision in seeking the high ground. It would have been better to have kept to the valleys where, whilst there might have been more danger of bumping into American patrols, they'd have had the advantage of some warning and the chance to decide whether to engage or withdraw.

As it was, here in this copse there was every likelihood that they were already surrounded, for if there was one Yank patrol up the forward slope of the hill then there could be others on the reverse slopes. And, whilst they might give Kleiser a sudden and unexpected pain in the arse, it would more or less mean curtains for the entire section.

But that need not be too bad, Scherfe told himself on reflection, providing Stumm would agree to throw down his MG-42 machine gun and call it a day. A few months in a Yank prisoner-of-war cage was a damn sight better than dying on this hillside. But Scherfe knew that there wasn't a chance in hell of Stumm surrendering to a squad of inexperienced American infantry. The traditions of the Grossdeutschland Division and his five endless years of conflict had long since driven any ideas of capitulation from Stumm's mind. The madman would stick to his damned MG-42 so long as he was still breathing and there was one round left in the breech!

So Scherfe crouched low in the long grass with his rifle on the ground in front of him and his MP-40 Schmeiser at his side, magazine fitted and mechanism cocked.

He knew the drill, all right.

Use the G-41 self-loading rifle with its high degree of accuracy to pick off any Yank head which popped up from beyond the dead ground ahead and then take up the Schmeiser if they came at him in a sudden mad rush. In his concealed position he would probably come off best in the face of a bayonet charge, for the Schmeiser was every bit as good as an MG-42 at close quarters. A frontal assault wasn't his problem. What worried him was the possibility of the Yanks coming at him from three or four different directions at the same time!

So Scherfe wiped the streaming sweat from his eyes and scanned the rough ground around him. At times like this his mind had an uneasy habit of flicking back to his home: to his mother and two sisters. There also came vivid mental pictures of the long garden behind the house which reached as far as the brook, the whole area rich in summer blooms and flowering shrubs. He guessed his subconscious provided it as some sort of antidote to the tensions which mounted inside him at the imminence of a battle he might not survive.

Could be that Kleiser, despite his dullness and lack of imagination, also had something which he could latch on to during surges of stress and panic. A wan smile broke across his down-covered cheeks as Scherfe contemplated what that might be, but then he shook his head. No chance at all! Kleiser just butted head-first into everything he ran up against. He didn't need any mental escape.

He was right, too! For Helmut Kleiser, with his broad back to the rest of the section and his weapons laid out in a pattern similar to Scherfe's, had nothing at all on his mind. He knew there was a possibility that some Yank infantryman might appear from the trees lower down the reverse slope, but he also knew that they'd first send over a scattering of mortar bombs or a flurry of small-arms fire. He'd have ample time to take up the battle — which also meant he could doze under the warm midday sun without having that bastard, Stumm, bawl him out.

'How're you making out, Franz?'

Kreutzmann looked up with a smile on his face and surprise evident in his eyes. It had probably been at some place like Kharkov when Klaus Stumm had last shown interest in his physical condition — and that at the time when Russian shrapnel had whisked away a couple of the ribs over his heart. Then, he guessed that Stumm had believed him to be a goner. He wondered if parallel thoughts were again in Stumm's mind.

He did his best to widen his smile, but the effort did little more than accentuate the man's weakening condition. The eyes appeared even duller in the pale, gaunt face; the mouth even more tortured.

'I'll make it!'

He replied with a force of conviction which, had it been dark, would have belied his appearance.

'All the same,' Stumm said curtly, 'we can't hang on here. Ammo's too low an' once the Yanks work round the flank we've no way out. I reckon we should have kept to the valleys!'

Kreutzmann looked doubtful. 'To the railway track? The Robichon line?'

Stumm shrugged.

'Maybe. It's no worse being pinned in a valley than on top of a hill. Robichon's already over an' forgotten, anyway.' He turned abruptly, calling across the distance to Kleiser. But the big man didn't stir.

'Kleiser!' he yelled again. Louder.

Kleiser's shoulders shook spasmodically.

'You were asleep you fat, idle bastard!'

Stumm's hand moved reflexively to the Luger automatic in the leather holster at his belt. At that range he could have picked off the man with a couple of shots. But Kleiser was now wide enough awake to see the movement and quick in slipping the strap of his MP-40 Schmeiser from his left shoulder.

Stumm's hand froze over the holster, but to Kreutzmann and Scherfe, watching the tension develop in front of them, it was apparent that much of the initial anger had left him. There had been those fleeting few seconds when he might have murdered Kleiser there and then, now the time was passed.

Kleiser seemed to sense both his escape and the fact that for a moment his life hadn't been worth a damn. He glanced down at the Schmeiser in his hand as though he hadn't put it there and then he threw the strap roughly back over his shoulder. Much as he loathed the sturmann, he wouldn't have attempted a confrontation like that one. Stumm would have drilled him through the heart before he'd even brought up the muzzle of his machine-pistol. He straightened the helmet across his forehead and lumbered to his feet, shrugging as he peered across the thirty odd metres to where Stumm was watching him with a hand still on the button of his holster.

'Sorry, sturmann!' Kleiser said as he closed the distance between them, keeping his voice low so that young Scherfe might not hear. 'The sun made me drowsy, but I wasn't asleep.' He forced a laugh. 'I know better than that, sturmann!' It was a form of apology which was unusual for Kleiser, but the man knew that if it ever came to meeting Stumm head-on, then he'd be wise to pick his own time. But then his voice hardened as he added, 'You should know by now I'm not stupid enough to leave a flank open.'

Stumm's eyes never left Kleiser's florid face. Sooner or later, this hulking farmhand must die by his hand; but, he too, would pick his time. And when that time came he'd make sure it didn't explode from something as bloody stupid as Kleiser nodding off on a hot afternoon.

'Here!' Stumm snarled at him. 'Take four of these belts. Put two round your neck an' give young Scherfe the other two. The fifth stays on the gun!'

Kleiser ambled over to where Kreutzmann was lying beside the MG-42 in his operational Number Two position. There he stooped to gather up the loaded ammunition belts into his great arms. A couple he slung round his neck. The others he draped over one arm, as though they had no weight at all, and crossed the short distance to Scherfe's position. It was only then that Stumm's reason for distributing the belts struck him. He looked back at Stumm with the incident of a few minutes earlier already at the back of his mind.

'Are we planning to pull out, Sturmann?'

But Stumm didn't answer the question. He merely pointed at Scherfe. 'Just move your bloody idle self. I'll give you a couple of minutes to get back to your position.'

For his part, Franz Kreutzman looked relieved.

Stumm hadn't been as indifferent to his condition as he'd imagined he would be. Now, without the weight of the loaded Spandau belts, he'd make better progress.

They watched Kleiser drop the belts on the ground beside Scherfe and as he turned round the sudden drumming of a Browning machine gun bit into the silence of the afternoon. Kleiser reacted on reflex and threw himself to the ground whilst Stumm and Kreutzmann listened to the hum of the heavy-calibre bullets as they swept through the treetops high above them. They didn't know that this was Lieutenant Roger Bailey's Number One Section sounding off with the first of their five second bursts under the control of Sergeant Abel Kalowski, but they *did* know they were safe from any random small-arms fire the Americans could throw at them. It made sense that if they couldn't reach the Yanks with their MG-42 and Schmeisers, then neither could the enemy reach them with their Brownings! Until the Americans did something positive the situation was stalemate.

Stumm watched more branches wafting idly down from the treetops and then turned again to Kleiser who, by this time, had sensed what was happening and was getting sheepishly to his feet. He kept his eyes averted from Stumm, his face even more florid than usual, his mouth twisting in anger that the sturmann had seen his frantic dive for cover.

As Kleiser ambled back to his position with the ammunition belts slipping untidily from his shoulders. Stumm spoke again to Kreutzmann.

'Franz!' he said with a note of finality. 'We'll move right now. The Yanks must have something brewing or they wouldn't have given us that burst. Are you ready?'

Kreutzmann nodded and painfully stood up, his face contorting over the grin he tried to put there. But Stumm made no effort to help him, instead turning his attention to the machine gun, leaving the loaded belt in the breech, clipping back the bipod legs and then heaving it up in his arms and sliding the strap over his right shoulder so that, if need be, he could use the weapon as a machine pistol. He then wound the ammunition belt round his right forearm.

He called across the distance to Rudi Scherfe who had been watching the preparations for withdrawal; but most of what he said was drowned in another burst of machine gun fire from down the slope. Stumm waited irritably as more branches dropped around him, at the same time smiling sardonically at the way the Americans wasted their ammunition. What would he give for a half of what they had fired pointlessly into the trees?

What were the stupid bastards trying to do, anyway?

Frighten him off with a trajectory which could only have been effective against low-flying aircraft? As the Browning spluttered into silence he called again to Scherfe.

'Go join Kleiser . . .!'

The words were barely out of his mouth when a red Very flare sizzled high above the trees to the right of the copse. The four Germans lifted their eyes to it as a man, watching it reach its zenith and then begin to drop into the trees, pouring a trail of white smoke.

Stumm was asking himself why he'd underestimated the Americans. It was clear now they hadn't been content to squat in the safety of their forward slope, hanging on either for night-fall or an artillery or air-strike. He'd underestimated their officer, too! The platoon had got some tactical manoeuvre under way.

Stumm slipped his right arm from the coil of the ammunition belt to let it spread over the ground at his feet, at the same time turning to the woodland as though half-expecting an infantry assault to come at them there and then. But his hesitation was only momentary, for he re-wound the belt with the speed he'd released it and set off at a good pace towards the rear of the copse, where Kleiser was now standing with his Schmeiser at his hip, as prepared for an attack as his sturmann.

But Stumm had not covered half the distance when a fusilade of small-arms fire from the forward slopes broke across the woodland in a rising crescendo. True to his orders, Sergeant Kalowski was using the maximum firepower of his two sections in a rapid-fire sequence which ricocheted off the surrounding hills with the weight and fury of a full division. Even so, the bullets were still only striking the tops of the trees, and this time Kleiser didn't so much as bow his shoulders.

Rudi Scherfe was moving across open ground when the first high-explosive bomb from Bailey's 2-inch platoon mortar landed. Considering that the target area was unsited, this was a commendable ranging attempt on the part of Private John Evans, for the bomb exploded only metres to the left of the copse. Scherfe, who had neither seen nor heard its approach, caught the full blast, which lifted him off his feet and hurled him headlong into the undergrowth.

Stumm spun round, eyes scanning the sky above their positions, for he knew that a good mortar man could keep seven or eight bombs in the air at any one time — all of them certain to pattern the same target area. When he looked to the spot where Scherfe had been standing he saw only the dark, shallow indentation in the earth, the thin rising column of black smoke, a tang of cordite already drifting to his nostrils.

'I'll see to him!'

This was Kreutzmann, leaning unsteadily on his rifle, like Stumm looking speculatively into the sky.

When Kreutzmann spoke, Stumm had been on the point of calling for him and Kleiser to make their way down the reverse slope of the hill. It wasn't a panzergrenadier section leader's job to molly-coddle wounded – it was to get on with the bloody war. But he changed his mind. Had it not been for Kreutzmann's condition he would have left Scherfe where he lay and headed for the lower ground – but he knew that within the next few days he was going to need a reliable Number Two on the MG-42 machine gun, and no way could he use Helmut Kleiser. Better let Kreutzmann find out now if the boy was still breathing.

But then a second mortar bomb landed, as quietly out of the blue as the first one, and exploded a couple of metres in front of Franz Kreutzmann, who made a futile attempt to raise his arms to protect his face before he was blasted on to his back.

In the undergrowth, Rudi Scherfe sprawled face down with heather and thistle spikes stabbing into his cheeks and lips. He lifted his face clear, shaking his head, and then reflexively went through a routine drill which he'd done many times before – whenever he'd felt the hot blast of high-explosive against his unprotected body. He moved his toes, his fingertips, then tested his full weight against his knees on the ground. Was he still in one piece? Had he taken the blast of a mortar bomb and by some miracle managed to get away with it?

'Thank Christ!'

He breathed the words not as an exclamation but as a supplication.

Maybe he had!

With the taught lines of panic fading from his face, he attempted to turn over on to his back when his left leg buckled beneath him. Apprehensively, he put a hand to the spot on his thigh where the pain was most acute and when he took it away he found it sticky with fresh blood. Close again to panic he sat upright in the heather, twisting his body to see the damage.

He imagined the kind of sickening wound he'd seen so many times on soldiers of both armies: the flesh criss-crossed with vicious shrapnel tears, a white expanse of bared bone through a welling of dark blood.

Vomit was beginning to rise in his throat as he steeled

89

himself for the shock, but all he found was a seven or eight centimetre rip in his trousers halfway up the back of his thigh. And when, with stiffened fingers, he dragged away the frayed edges of the cloth he revealed no more than a cut in his flesh half the length of the tear. This was a clean and narrow incision; as neat as if it had been made with a sharp knife. The only blood was a few beads which were beginning to form along its length.

His fingers moved to the edges of the wound, but there were no sudden twinges of pain at the contact. The lump of shrapnel, which could have been the size of half the mortar bomb casing, had done no more than nick his flesh. The wound didn't even need sticking plaster.

So he had made it! He bloody well had!

He had begun to crawl to where his rifle and Schmeiser machine pistol were lying when the second bomb hit the ground. Again it was close enough for him to feel the shock waves, and when he raised his head to the explosion he saw Franz Kreutzmann spread-eagled on his back with his face already a bloody mask.

Scherfe froze.

Christ! Not Kreutzmann!

Kreutzmann was as indestructible as Stumm himself. Kreutzmann couldn't be knocked out by a random mortar bomb from this half-baked Yank platoon. Not Franz Kreutzmann who'd survived Kharkov and all that the Russians had been able to throw at him over a two year campaign.

And what about the battles of the past two months which they'd fought as a section? What about the personal spark of camaraderie he'd shared with Kreutzmann – his one and only link with rationality under Stumm's weird command?

What about the Grossdeutschland tradition?

Kreutzmann couldn't die in this God-forsaken forest which wasn't even marked on the map. This was no place for a soldier to die – not for an SS panzergrenadier fighting a war that wasn't really a part of the big war! Not in a half-hearted skirmish with a green American infantry platoon. Kreutzmann couldn't die as pointlessly as this, could he?

Besides, how would Stumm react?

The sudden thought chilled young Scherfe. Stumm, who was already at breaking point and only a hair's breadth from insanity. Would Stumm attempt to lead his survivors into some mad, suicidal charge against the American machine guns?

Warily, Scherfe got to his feet, still crouching low, anticipating anything from a flurry of mortar bombs to a full-scale frontal bayonet assault. But there was only the still body of Franz Kreutzmann a few metres in front of him. When he shot a glance farther down the copse he saw Stumm with the MG-42 machine gun slung at the hip. Kleiser, not a great distance away, was staring at Kreutzmann's body with his mouth open and evidently experiencing the same kind of reaction as Scherfe himself had felt.

'How's Kreutzmann?'

This was Stumm, angry and impatient, but the aggressive tone of voice relieved Scherfe. Stumm wasn't going berserk and chopping down everything that moved in his path. It seemed that with this tight little battle still squarely on his shoulders, Stumm was being a soldier. Thank God for the Grossdeutschland!

Scherfe went over to where Kreutzmann lay, and when he saw the lower half of the man's face his eyes froze there in horror. The bottom jaw had gone completely. So had the tongue. The cheeks had been torn so that the edges of the wound were frayed, just like the cloth of his own uniform where the shrapnel had ripped it.

The teeth of the upper jaw appeared startlingly white against the bloody dark hole that was the man's open throat.

Indecisive, Scherfe turned again to where Stumm was standing in a silent bid for orders; but at that distance it was obvious that Stumm was unable to see what had happened to his Number Two. Scherfe looked back at Kreutzmann's hideous wound. The man was going to die soon and slowly. Eventually, he'd choke from a congestion of blood seeping into his lungs. Drown in his own blood!

It would be humane to finish him off here and now rather than leave him to the Americans who would have no more means of coping with such a terrible wound than they had. Stumm would understand so much. Indecisive, he made a reflex movement with his machine pistol, but Kreutzmann noticed it and dug a hand into the holster at his waist from which he pulled out his Luger automatic. With it he waved Scherfe away. Still the boy hesitated and it was only when Kreutzmann pushed the muzzle into the roof of his upper jaw that Scherfe stooped to snatch up the spare barrel for the MG-42 and hurried down the slope to join Stumm and Kleiser.

He had covered less than a dozen metres when the shot rang out, distinct above the intermittent fire from the American platoon; but Scherfe didn't look back. Kreutzmann was gone for all time and he found himself wondering about the photograph of the dark-haired woman and the small child which the man had kept so secretly in the breast pocket of his tunic.

Neither did Stumm question Scherfe, but led them at a steady jog-trot farther down the reverse slope of the hill. They were on the point of turning amongst the tall trees when a second red Very flare soared high over the copse behind them. And with it there came more mortar bombs and a renewed concentration of American small-arms fire. There followed the half-hearted cries of American infantry as they launched themselves into their first bayonet assault – against an already abandoned enemy position.

Twenty-four hours earlier, north of the village of St Jouin and fifteen kilometres east of Robichon-sur-Florentin, a group of four men and one woman crouched in a sun-dried ditch on a rising spur of ground some fifty metres south of the narrow-gauge railway track. The woman clutched a pair of binoculars in lean, sunburned hands; the men had German MP-40 Schmeiser machine pistols resting across their knees. Magazines were loaded, safety chains forward. Beside one of the younger men was a small, hand-operated electrical generator from which green, insulated wires led through the long grass to the railway track.

As time passed the group turned repeatedly to each other with anxious, questioning glances. The sun, dazzling to their eyes, reflected from the rock outcrop of the embankment across the way and above it, a shimmering heat haze blurred their vision.

The leader, a youngish man whose slim fingers were now checking over the mechanism of the generator, frowned impatiently as he once again glanced at the watch on his wrist. He was Michel Menton, a lecturer in economics at the École Polytechnique, Argentan.

The group had been in position now for the best part of an hour and the train load of Waffen SS from Robichon-sur-Florentin was taking far too long to cover the fifteen kilometres to their ambush point.

They had assembled quickly, shocked into action at the news of the wanton massacre at the Robichon halt, telephoned to the Confrérie Headquarters by a Robichon farmer who had stumbled upon the scene and found the telephone still connected.

Now they were considering whether this scum of Waffen SS murderers had changed their minds about using the two-carraige train to bludgeon a path through the thinly-spaced American reconnaissance units and had taken to the hills instead, seeking security rather than speed. This was a real possibility and the group grew angry at the thought of a quick and decisive revenge being snatched from their grasp.

'We'd better begin looking to our backs!' Menton commented. 'Perhaps we're the ones in the hot seat!'

But the woman shook her head.

She was a slightly-built girl in her early twenties wearing a pretty, pale blue summer dress with a black belt, her thick dark hair hiding most of her face as she moved her head.

'It's unlikely,' she said quietly, 'the Boches have far more to worry about than chasing odd detachments from the *réseau*.' She shrugged. 'Now it's their turn to fear us!'

Her name was Françoise Dolent. She had been the group's Intelligence officer for the past six months and was proud of her responsibilities. Particularly now that the course of the war had swung towards the Allies. She added, 'The SS wouldn't have taken the train if they didn't want it. The killing at Robichon could have been incidental, but they still needed the train.' She shrugged again, as though the basic military strategy of the Waffen SS was unconnected with the job in hand. She even managed a smile in an attempt to ease the tension. 'Could be we're being too impatient, Michel.'

He smiled back at her as though she could be right, then glanced at the three other members of his group who returned it ruefully, saying nothing as they shifted position uncomfortably in the ditch, wiping the sweat from their faces and the dazzling oil-sheen from the blue steel of their weapons.

'Could be they're expecting the *réseau* to be waiting,' young Dominic Charais said a moment later.

'Better still for us if the bastards are marching!'

This was Dominic's father who, thirty years earlier, had fought at Verdun, Ypres and Beaumont Hamel. He grinned affectionately at his son as he spoke, immensely proud that a boy of seventeen should have the temperament for humour at the time of his baptism of fire with the Confrérie de Normandie.

Nevertheless, the older man meant what he said. Buried beneath the aggregate ballast alongside the railway track was upwards of forty kilos of gelignite – provided by British Special

93

Operations Executive for just such an occasion as this.

Under such a charge of high-explosive, heavy enough to lift the locomotive and its carriages high off the lines, he would have preferred to have seen the soft bodies of German panzergrenadiers take the full blast. Then there would have been no need for the detachment to use their Schmeisers against survivors. Without the steel frames of the carriages to shield them, there would be no survivors! And that was too good for the murdering bastards who'd mown down helpless women and children at the Robichon halt.

The fourth man in the group lifted a hand to shield his eyes and stared down the shimmering line of railway track.

'Still nothing!' he announced, 'neither train nor marching Boches.'

It was merely said for something to say because talking helped boost his morale at such times as this. He was Jules Rimeau, who had kept a small grocery store in the Rue Cochet in Argentan until the tightening of domestic rationing had enforced its closure. Now he was unemployed and in constant dread that he might be conscripted by the Germans for forced labour under the Reléve scheme. This, more than anything else, had encouraged his work with the Confrérie de Normandie. Recently his wife, Bernice, had become employed as a cleaner at the Wehrmacht-occupied Boulevard d'Ingouville Barracks, which had given him enough cover to set his mind at rest.

Suddenly his eyes widened and he squirmed out of the ditch with an ear close to the ground.

'Listen! Listen!' There was a hoarse urgency to his voice. 'Michel! For God's sake listen.'

Alongside him, old Guy Charais shook his head and smiled tolerantly.

'It's the breeze through the trees Jules, my friend. There is nothing.' He pointed westwards along the line. 'As you said yourself, neither train nor marching Boches!'

But the girl clambered out of the ditch as Rimeau had done, lying flat on the outcrop with her binoculars to her eyes. As Guy had said, there was nothing to see; but seconds later the sounds which the sharp ears of Jules Rimeau had picked up were beginning to reach her. She turned quickly to Menton whose face remained impassive, his concentration still focused on the hand generator in front of him.

Then he nodded. The sound was now identifiable. Unmistakably so! The measured chug-chug-chug-chug of a steam locomotive making hard going with a heavy load against the gradient.

When he glanced around the group they answered with smiles of relief. So, after all, their crazy dash to this cutting in the outcrop, the hazards of burying the gelignite and laying the cables to the detonators had not been for nothing.

At the time, they had all recognised that the risks they were taking did by no means guarantee success. Some passing Wehrmacht patrol, or even a rabble of German deserters, might have seen them in the cutting and gunned them down for no other reason than they looked like French Resistance. No questions would have been asked. The Germans would have opened fire with automatic weapons at a long range and that would have been that.

Michel Menton's plan was uncomplicated: an orthodox routine which the Confrérie had used to remove enemy marching troops and convoys since the start of the occupation.

As soon as the main explosive charge had detonated, machine guns would enfilade the front of the train and then, as survivors panicked to the rear, the rest of the automatic weapons would cut off their escape. They had no intention of engaging the Waffen SS from their ditch above the railway track. If it should happen that there were enemy survivors, then Guy Charais would pick these off one at a time with a sniper's rifle fitted with telescopic sights.

Above all, the revenge of the Confrérie de Normandie must be as merciless and as complete as the SS massacre at the Robichon halt had been. Their dead and mutilated bodies were to be left where they lay amongst the shattered debris of the French train. Thus, the awful tableau would be complete for all Germans passing that way to see: the innocent French civilians dead at the halt and, a few kilometres farther along the line, evidence of the price the murderers had had to pay!

The rumble of the slowly approaching train was becoming more distinct with every passing second, the sound carried ahead on the breeze.

Jules Rimeau still had his binoculars to his eyes.

'I see the engine,' he told them calmly, 'Just coming into the long straight.'

Menton confirmed.

'I see it, too!' He shot a quick glance at his wristwatch. 'That should give us fifty seconds at the most.' He grinned at Guy Charais. 'Let's hope the detonators are dry and that we got the wiring right eh, Guy?' And Charais grinned back, the confidence in the man's eyes telling Menton that there was no need to worry.

But then Charais added 'If we haven't, then it looks like we've got a hell of fight on our hands, Michel!'

They spaced themselves out into their allocated positions along the short length of the ditch, crouching low amongst the loose stones, pressing their bodies against the clay of the forward side, preparing themselves for an explosion which would bring debris raining down on their heads.

Only Menton remained standing, observing the railway track through the long, waving grass. He was thinking that if he'd had his way he'd have sited the position a further twenty or thirty metres from the track. But when he had put this to Guy Charais, the old man had smiled and shaken his head, maintaining that the longer the connecting wires the greater the chance of electrical failure. Also, after the explosion they needed to use their Schmeisers at a minimum killing range.

Not one survivor! Remember! Not one! That was how this ambush had to be – as complete as Robichon!

Menton clasped a hand firmly on the black enamelled magnets of the generator, pushing the machine down hard against the earth, the other taking the cranking handle between thumb and first two fingers. He checked the speed at which he could make a half-dozen turns and, with the train less than a half-kilometre away, he took a couple of seconds to see how Françoise Dolent was making out a few metres to his right.

He wasn't surprised to find her eyes on him and she smiled up at him and shrugged at her inescapable commitment. He nodded his understanding. She was right. There could be no turning back now. Victory or death would follow in the next minute and it would all depend on this old generator beneath his hand and whether or not there was a break in the fifty metre lengths of cable which connected it to the detonator and the explosive charge . . . Françoise Dolent, youngest daughter of Dr Étien Dolent who had a small country practice near Argentan. One day, if they were lucky, they would marry . . .

It was certain that the Waffen SS would be expecting reprisals and would be taking no chances. The train would be bristling with machine guns and there would be panzergrenadiers riding the locomotive and the tops of the two carriages, their equipment bulging with stick grenades. With such a show of force they would hope to scare off attackers, including not only wandering bands of French Resistance, but also isolated detachments of American infantry. They'd know there was little likelihood of attack from armour and would be taking a chance that the momentum and firepower of the train would bludgeon them through any American reconnaissance screen.

As it drew closer, Menton saw that he had been right in his assessment. This was what amounted to an armoured train. The windows had been knocked out and from them protruded the muzzles of MG-42 machine guns and MP-40 Schmeiser machine pistols. Inside the carriages men were standing-to their weapons, hands clutching laced belts of ammunition, their coal-scuttle helmets low over their brows against the sun, all looking highly operational – even in their vulnerability.

On the footboards and also squatting on top of the piled logs in the tender, more panzergrenadiers were riding with an arrogant self-assurance – as though they were still mounted on their Panzer MK VI Tigers. But the ragged condition of their uniforms and the haggard lines etched into their faces showed clearly even at that distance.

Menton's lips curled.

Boches scum!

The dregs of a defeated army which could only give vent to its chagrin and disillusionment through the pitiless killing of French women and children.

Why did these Boches swine keep on kidding themselves they were a master race? Because Adolf Hitler was still preaching that same crazy kind of propaganda? Because he was threatening the generals of Oberkommando Wehrmacht with a firing squad if they allowed one more SS battalion to withdraw from the Normandy battle front? Because demoralised infantry would rather kill or be killed than let the French see them panicking from the bite of the victorious American 3rd Army?

Probably a culmination of all these things, he reflected . . . the train was getting very close now and picking up speed after the gradient . . . twenty seconds left, maybe, and it would be over the gelignite charge . . . thank God a German was driving the locomotive! He could glimpse the soldier's helmet! Could have been that the Boches had high-jacked the engineer as well as his train, and that would have meant the *réseau* having to sacrifice a fellow-countryman.

Menton found his hands were sticky with a sweat as they pressed the generator harder into the ground. There was also a trembling sensation in his chest which he put down to fear. His lips were dry and his tongue seemed to have swollen to clog his mouth. He wanted to take another look at Françoise Dolent before he detonated the charge, but there was no time for that now. Ten seconds and closing: nine ... eight ... seven ... !

How many men would die when he spun that handle? How many? He'd no idea. A platoon? Two platoons? An infantry company? Upwards of a hundred human beings? Jesus, forgive me!

Five seconds. Four. Three!

The panzergrenadiers were sitting relaxed in the carriages and aboard the locomotive, reassured in that they had covered over thirty kilometres without incident and knowing there wasn't much farther to go. The line terminated with buffers at Longville Station five kilometres short of the Dives river.

The chug of the locomotive and the clank of the carriage wheels were now concentrated within the narrow cutting ... two seconds!

One second!

ZERO!

Calmly and deliberately, Michel Menton cranked the handle of the generator. One turn. Two. Three!

Nothing happened.

God! The train was speeding over the charge!

Frenziedly he jerked himself upright in the ditch, bending over the generator and cranking it with all the strength he could thrown into his wrists ...

The five members of the *réseau* had widely different impressions of what happened next.

Seventeen-year-old Dominic Charais, in his blooding with the Confrérie de Normandie, had been eager to see the immediate effect of his first ambush and had raised his head at the sound of the train entering the cutting and it was he, alone, who witnessed the full fury of the explosion, for Menton had had his eyes clamped on the generator.

But young Dominic with his healthy face flushed with pride and anticipation had not watched for long. Seconds later that same face, chalk-white, was buried in the clay of the bank against which he sprawled with streams of vomit coursing down his jacket in sticky strands. In those few seconds he had learned that war could be as horrifying for the victors as for the defeated.

There had been little blast from the exploding gelignite, muffled by the shape and position of the hole beneath the ballast in which it had been buried and by the dampening effect of the carriages. Dominic recalled a sudden sheet of orange flame, vivid even under the glare of the sun. Then there had been a couple of seconds when nothing seemed to happen at all and during which the train travelled a few more metres. Then, with a great rending tear, the first carriage disintegrated before his eyes. He had vague recollections of a couple of bogey wheels, still attached to their axle, spinning fully fifty metres into the air to tumble back to earth like a crazy diabolo. In their wake fell pieces of the carriages and locomotive and a ghastly rain of human bodies.

In his young mind he had never considered that the bodies of SS panzergrenadiers could be infinitely more fragile than the train in which they were travelling. His eyes widened in horror as he watched human torsos and limbs, copiously streaming blood, soar in the sky above him. It was then that he turned away, seeking reassurance from his friends who had witnessed such things before; but, when he looked at Françoise Dolent, he saw that her black hair and summer dress were already splashed with blood from the sky. Fresh nausea gripped him and, sick and fainting, he closed his eyes.

His father, Guy Charais, farther along the ditch had kept his head down, counting up to five after the explosion before crawling out, his calibrated Canadian Ross sniper's rifle with the telescopic sights cradled in his arms. He knew his job all right and, no matter what happened to the train, he would lie in the grass and patiently pick off any Waffen SS still fit enough to make it as far as the outcrop bank of the cutting.

The near bank was not his responsibility. Rimeau, Françoise and Dominic were to contain any threat from that angle with their Schmeiser machine pistols. So, old Guy slipped forward the safety catch and squirmed himself into a comfortable firing position with the Canadian Ross at his shoulder. It was only when he took time to peer down on to the railway track that he froze in much the same way that his son had done.

Incredibly, the track was almost clear of debris. Even the locomotive was a good metre from the lines, lying on its side like some great wounded animal. But, surprisingly, the boiler had not burst in the explosion and a thin column of steam curled lazily skywards from the domed brass safety valve midway along the boiler. The fuel logs had tipped out of the tender and burning wood from the firebox had set them ablaze. Threatening eddies of black smoke, curling and fanned by the breeze, were already edged with flame which flickered around the bodies of the dead and wounded panzergrenadiers who had been riding the locomotive. Many of them were little more than sticky looking puddles of bloody pulp, but there were others who had been pinned under the weight of the locomotive by arms and legs and whose faces were contorted in soundless agony at the horror of their wounds and the searing heat of the fire slowly creeping towards them.

Charais's hard lips twisted sardonically as he took in the scene of death and devastation. The yellow rock of the outcrop across the track was splashed haphazardly with blood, which glistened crimson-bright in the sun. There were also limbs and lumps of flesh, some large enough to be identifiable even at that distance, but there was nothing alive and moving!

Charais lowered the rifle and jerked himself into an upright position, looking at Michel Menton and shrugging.

Menton nodded his agreement with a pale, tense face. Charais's message didn't need spelling out. There would be no Waffen SS survivors to take up positions across the way.

Jules Rimeau joined Charais in his role of covering the near embankment and when he caught the older man's eyes he recognised in them a reaction which echoed his own.

Their victory against the Waffen SS – their greatest victory in the three years' turbulent history of the Confrérie de Normandie – was complete. But, somehow no one was cheering.

Why was that?

Why weren't they wringing each other's hands? Why weren't they slapping each other on the back? Surely this was one victory to celebrate. Then why weren't they celebrating?

It was Françoise Dolent who gave them the answer. With fresh German blood which had fallen from the sky still seeping through her hair on to her summer dress, she left her position in the ditch and walked silently over to where Michel Menton was standing.

There she took his hand in hers and turned him away from the devastation of the cutting towards the green fields to the south where the sun and the breeze caught the lush foliage of the trees that was France and where no fragmented German bodies oozed their blood.

Chapter Six

*Digest of a Communique issued by Oberkommando
Wehrmacht, Paris, to Reichsfuhrer Adolf Hitler
Date: 3rd August 1944
Signatory:
Oberbefehlshaber West: Generalfeldmarschall
Gunter von Kluge*

*During the past twenty-four hours there have been determined
attacks by spearhead reconnaissance battle groups of the
United States 3rd Army. These have generally been concentrated within an area from the western limits of the Severs
forest to the town of Brécey which fell to the enemy late last
evening and is now being aggressively counter-
attacked in strength by units of our 116th Panzer
Division.*

*Battles are also developing in the surrounding area of Sée
which town the Americans are threatening in an all out
assault; but reports indicate that our 275th Division has so far
been successful in containing these attacks. In addition, to the
north, American armoured probes are astride the Avranches-
Mortain highway heading towards the small town of Juvigny-
le-Tetre, evidently seeking the high ground to the north of
Mortain. To counter, units of our 84th Division are
establishing defensive strongpoints west of St Barthélémy.*

After their skirmish with the American infantry platoon,
Stumm had led Kleiser and Scherfe down the reverse slope of
the hill from the copse at a steady jog-trot, the heavy MG-42
machine gun balanced easily on his right shoulder as though it
had no weight at all.

Kleiser was blowing hard, even on the down gradient, and
young Scherfe was suffering pains he hadn't expected from the
shrapnel scratch in his thigh. But only when they had dropped

deep into the valley and it was certain that the Americans were not chasing did Stumm slacken his pace. They were still in thickish woodland and, discounting the possibility of ambushes, were well screened from the surrounding hills.

Presently, Stumm changed course into a more easterly direction, partly so they could cling to the contours of the valley, but mainly because none of them had any idea how far the forest stretched. Also, with a total of three men in the group there was nothing to be gained by attempting to maintain a battle formation with one man out in front and another covering the rear. The best plan was to keep moving eastwards and hope for the best.

Scherfe, hard on Stumm's heels with the two MG-42 ammunition belts slung round his neck, had taken it for granted that he was to be Number Two on the machine gun though Stumm had said nothing since they'd broken contact with the Americans. Yet there had been something decisive in the way the sturmann had ignored Kleiser, indicating Scherfe to follow. Whether Kleiser was angry at this, Scherfe didn't know; nor did he know if the big man had ever expected to take over the dead Kreutzmann's role.

As he stumbled through the thick grass after Stumm, Scherfe told himself there hadn't been a chance in hell of this happening, but Kleiser was too dumb to realise it and probably believed that his battle experience along the Pas de Calais would influence Stumm's decision.

There was also something else to thing about – Stumm could be building up tension as a result of Kreutzmann's death. Because he hadn't reacted yet didn't mean he wasn't going to!

Now the noise of battle to the south and the north had become less distracting, though large numbers of aircraft were constantly passing overhead, thundering by unseen, screened by the thick foliage. But the blast of their bombs caused frequent changes in air pressure which soughed through the trees like a sudden gale.

Stumm halted after an hour, his lean face streaming sweat, his breathing relaxed and controlled. In contrast, Kleiser was bending heavily over his rifle with open mouth as he gasped for air, the thick reddish hair poking from beneath his helmet and sweat stuck to his cheeks. He was looking apprehensive, too, his small eyes darting from Stumm to Scherfe and back again. It suddenly dawned on Scherfe what was probably at the back of the man's mind. The stupid sod could be working up something to say to Stumm about Kreutzmann.

He moved forward instinctively, intending to edge his body between the two of them before Kleiser could speak the words that could earn him a bullet through the heart, but Stumm swept him aside with a powerful sweep of his forearm.

Scherfe regained his balance to find the sturmann's eyes riveted on Kleiser.

'Don't you say it, you ugly bastard!' Stumm snarled, venom flashing in his blue eyes. 'Just don't you dare mention his name!'

Kleiser froze where he stood, uncomprehending, in his dim unimaginative way grasping at what he had thought was a chance to heal the rift between the sturmann and himself by saying that Kreutzmann's death was a hell of a tragedy. Despite Stumm's reaction, he did his best to put a grin on his face. Stumm must have misunderstood...

'I was going to say...'

'Mention his name an' you're a dead man, Kleiser!'

That caught Kleiser up short and he turned to Scherfe with eyes smouldering with resentment. Couldn't a feller say he was sorry any more when a pal got himself knocked off? But Scherfe was shaking his head expressively from side to side and only then did Kleiser comprehend.

With dusk, the clouds thickened over the valley and the threat of more rain came with a cold, northerly breeze.

'We'll seek higher ground,' Stumm decided and they headed across the foot of the valley to where an escarpment rose sheer for twenty or thirty metres into more woodland. At its base they came upon shallow, blackened hollow amongst the vegetation, around which the grass was singed yellow and the earth charred and pulverised. The acrid stench of cordite hit their nostrils.

Mortar bombs!

Stumm slowed his pace and motioned Scherfe to his left and Kleiser to his right. They were asking themselves who had caused those mortar craters. Apparently there had been some sort of a battle at the foot of the escarpment and that meant there could still be wounded lying around with fingers on the triggers of their automatic weapons and enough pain and chagrin in their hearts to shoot on sight.

They moved on in the new formation at the same deliberate pace, Stumm with the MG-42 slung from his right shoulder and a half-loaded ammunition belt clipped into the breech and trailing over his right forearm. Kleiser and Scherfe also held their Schmeisers at the hip, the short-barrelled machine pistols more manoeuvrable and deadlier at close quarters than the heavy Spandau.

Here and there on the ground were copious bloodstains, but there were no signs of bodies either alive or dead. Perhaps some patrol, hugging the escarpment for cover, had been surprised by an enemy across the valley who had thrown a mortar barrage at them on the chance of random casualties?

Certainly there had been casualties, for they came across more blood and Scherfe picked up an empty pack of Camel cigarettes. But that didn't mean that Americans had been on the receiving end of the bombardment, for the SS had taken enough Yank loot during their early battles around the Utah and Omaha beaches to keep them stocked in personal comforts for the rest of the year.

'Sturmann!'

Kleiser's sharp cry caused the other two to swing round with fingers tightening on their triggers; but when they spotted Kleiser they saw he was bending over into a clump of undergrowth. He straightened up, grinning broadly. In one hand he held his Schmeiser by the barrel, in the other a bloody mass of fur and raw flesh.

'What the hell have you got there?'

There was the customary snarl of irritation in Stumm's voice which edged in whenever he spoke to the big man, but now he also showed raw anger that Kleiser had been stupid enough to bawl across a valley which would reverberate the sound and pinpoint their position for any lookout who might be on stand-to.

But Kleiser, in his oblivion, was still grinning.

'Rabbits, Sturmann!' he yelled. 'Three of 'em and none the worse for a bit o' mortar blast!'

That night they found themselves a cave in the face of that same escarpment. The sky had clouded solid with nightfall and the rain which had threatened when they had first entered the valley spewed down in sheets, cascading over the outcrop into the wooded foothills where the mortar bombs had exploded.

But in the cave the three Germans were dry and ravenously hungry with an appetising smell of warm food drifting about them – the first fresh meat they had tasted in weeks.

Even Stumm had become less aggressive towards the ex-farmhand as he watched him expertly skin and cut up the three shrapnel-mauled rabbits, pausing now and then to pick out pieces of metal and holding them up for the other two to see before tossing them over his shoulder to the back of the cave. Kleiser had miraculously found sufficient dry wood to get a fire going, spearing the pieces of meat on bayonets and barbecueing them slowly over the glowing charcoal.

Stumm had spread his gas cape over the dusty floor of the cave and dissembled the MG-42 machine gun, meticulously laying out the parts in order of reassembly, wiping them with rag before sparsely oiling them and setting them down again in that same precise pattern.

As Scherfe watched him, the boy decided to follow suit and began to strip down his own Schmeiser. At that, Stumm lifted his head with a glint of humour in his eyes.

'You getting the idea there's more to soldiering than filling your belly, Scherfe?' he asked, at which Scherfe did his best to grin, never sure how he should take Stumm's random jibes or what the sturmann was likely to follow up with. Scherfe's thoughts were still fixed on the death of Franz Kreutzmann.

He acknowledged and no more, playing it safe.

Stumm was holding out a hand, fingers moving impatiently.

'Then give me the spare barrel!'

Scherfe turned to his haversack, from which he pulled out the spare barrel of the MG-42 which he had shoved longways beneath the two leather fastening straps.

He handed it to Stumm, thinking that maybe the sturmann had changed his mind about who was to be Number Two on the machine gun. Could be that Kleiser's lucky find of the slaughtered rabbits had redeemed the big man. Not that Scherfe cared. Being Number Two on an MG-42 demanded dedicated involvement. There could be no chance of loping off on your own when a battle began to turn the wrong way: with Stumm manipulating the trigger he'd be committed until the sturmann decided it was time to move.

Besides, machine guns invariably attracted enemy mortar fire, squirts from flame throwers and salvoes from anti-tank guns as well as from artillery. And when tanks got close enough they'd recently developed a nasty habit of spinning their tracks on machine gun emplacements and churning the gunners and their weapons into the ground. Kleiser could be a candidate for that and welcome!

'Like a pig's arse!'

'Sturmann?' Scherfe jerked himself out of his introspection to see Stumm squinting down the rifling of the MG-42 spare barrel into Kleiser's fire.

'When are you planning to clean this, Scherfe?'

Stumm threw the barrel at him so hard that when Scherfe reached out a hand, more to protect his face than catch it, the flash eliminator hit his knuckles and it clattered against the wall of the cave behind him.

Despite the sudden surge of pain, Scherfe spun round to snatch it from the floor. Now he was beginning to watch the sturmann more warily. Out of the corner of his eye, he sensed that Kleiser had also dragged his attention away from his cooking and was showing interest: they both knew that the spare barrel had been Franz Kreutzmann's responsibility.

So why was Stumm pushing him?

Even in the half-light of the fire Scherfe could detect that same crazy gleam in Stumm's blue eyes. Crouching there with the red glare highlighting his thick blond hair and the pieces of his machine gun spread out around him, the man looked like some satanic priest about to perform an unholy rite.

For the first time he began to sense how Kleiser felt under the constant threat of Stumm's intolerance and the certainty that the sturmann could react to a wild gesture or even a wrong word.

He swallowed hard, seeking words that might chase away Kreutzmann's ghost from Stumm's warped mind.

'Maybe I can boil out both barrels after we've eaten, Stur-mann?'

'Have you enough wood to boil water, Kleiser?'

Momentarily, Kleiser floundered at unexpectedly becoming involved and his face showed it. But he was quick to answer.

'Yes, sturmann! Of course, sturmann! I'll get more wood!'

That night, Kleiser and Scherfe slept uneasily despite the soothing effect of warm food and the dry comfort of the cave.

Scherfe lay for an hour and more with eyes wide open, staring through the narrow entrance at the ragged silhouettes of trees on to which the rain deluged. There were few other sounds. Now and then the distant rumble of heavy artillery broke upon the silence of the night, but there were no indications of any infantry involvement. He guessed that the change in the weather might have come as something of a salvation to both armies and given them a good reason to consolidate whatever gains or losses they'd made that day.

But Scherfe knew that he was as apprehensive of Klaus Stumm as he was of American shells and aircraft which sought only to destroy his young body. Stumm was living on a fast-burning fuse and sooner or later he'd explode. Kreutzmann had known this, too, and had always been on hand to lead

Stumm back from the brink whenever he got too close. But now Kreutzmann was gone and Stumm brittle and unprotected.

If only the man would talk! A few curt orders now and then, fringed with cutting sarcasm, was the most they could ever get from him.

To Scherfe, his only chance of survival was by way of a confrontation between Stumm and Kleiser from which Kleiser came out on top!

It was about four am when Stumm began to scream. Frenzied banshee screams which tore across the splatter of pouring rain like calls from the dead. Kleiser and Scherfe jerked awake with hearts pounding, sleep-clogged eyes trying to pierce the darkness. They instinctively snatched at their weapons, both certain that an American patrol had infiltrated along the foot of the escarpment and was murdering Stumm where he slept. But as they crouched in indecision the screaming went on, the same wild, chilling, animal cries that burst from the man's soul.

It was Kleiser who first found a match and its sudden spurt of yellow flame flooded the cave with the abrupt intensity of a searchlight. Stumm lay flat on his back, arms stretched rigid above his head, his legs stiff as though he were reaching out with his toes. His face was screwed into an unrecognisable mask of terror, jaw contorted, tongue clawing at the roof of his mouth, lips curled back from bared teeth.

Scherfe dug into his tunic pocket for a stub of candle which he tossed to Kleiser and the big man put the dying match to the wick. Only then did they turn to each other, their expressions for once telling the same story: Stumm had reached his breaking point.

His five endless years of war from the rout of the British Expeditionary Force from Dunkirk; his soul-destroying battles across the Russian steppes with his famed Grossdeutschland Division; his fiinal battles from the Contentin Peninsula to this cave somewhere to the east of Normandy – all had taken their toll.

Kleiser shook his head, wanting no part in what was happening to their sturmann and that caused Scherfe to turn on him angrily. Even so, a note of uncertainty crept into his voice which he couldn't hide.

'What'll we do when we wakes up?' he asked, and that caused Kleiser to push himself awkwardly to his feet and cross the rock floor to where Stumm lay.

There he unbuttoned Stumm's holster and took out the Luger automatic, staring down impassively into the mad, screaming face, as though he had somehow managed to clear the sound from his senses. He took the kommando knife from its sheath and tossed it to Scherfe, before sliding away the heavy MG-42 machine gun from Stumm's side.

Now Stumm's screams were dissolving into discords of incoherent chatter, interspersed with rational commands and sudden, frantic shrieks of pain. There followed fitful movements of the rigid arms and legs as though the man were trying to run from the terrors of his dreams.

As Kleiser moved back to the rear of the cave cradling the MG-42 in his arms, Scherfe breathed a sigh of relief.

At the same time it struck Kleiser that this was the first time he'd ever handled the machine gun and that Stumm was likely to raise hell when he found it gone from his side. He shot an inquiring glance at Scherfe at the possibility and relief showed on his face as the boy nodded his approval. Only then did it cross Kleiser's mind that their sturmann might not be rational when he woke up — whenever that might be!

They remained awake until Stumm's tensions eased and it was an hour later that his limbs suddenly relaxed and he turned over on to his side with an enormous sigh. Minutes later he began to snore and Scherfe moved over to him, lifting the thick blond hair from his forehead and finding that much of the strain had also gone from his face. Stumm was sleeping.

'Kreutzmann!' Kleiser said. 'It was Kreutzmann buying it that tipped him over.'

Scherfe nodded. 'That *finally* tipped him, you mean.'

They agreed to sleep in rotation during the few remaining hours of darkness. When Scherfe awoke he found Kleiser was still sleeping noisily at the back of the cave and that Stumm, his Luger and kommando knife as well as the MG-42, were missing.

Savagely he kicked at Kleiser's shin and the big man jerked awake, a hand grasping automatically for his Schmeiser machine pistol until he was able to assimilate what was going on around him. When he saw only Scherfe sitting there he did no more than utter an obscenity and close his eyes again.

Scherfe lashed out with his boot again.

'Stumm's gone!'

The sudden surge of anger which had crossed Kleiser's eyes immediately changed to alarm. He sat bolt upright, a great hand pulverising the stiffness of sleep from his face.

'Gone?' he echoed. 'Gone where?'

'How the hell do I know?' he snarled back at him. 'You were supposed to be watching him, not me!'

But despite his sudden vent of anger, Scherfe sensed a rising elation as a new thought suddenly struck him. With Stumm out of the way it would be simple enough to dodge the dim-witted Kleiser and find a way to see the rest of the war through the way he wanted it. There'd be no more following Stumm blindly from one crisis to the next, turning every minute of every day into a bid for survival. He might even eke out the Normandy campaign in this same cave, living on hillside vegetation. Maybe he'd even be lucky enough to bag himself some game for he'd still have his rifle and ammunition.

Then, when the Americans consolidated, he'd take off his helmet and tunic, throw away his weapons and quietly give himself up. That sounded a damn sight better than being a dead panzergrenadier!

Hope began to flood inside him. Some happy day there might even be a chance of seeing his mother and sisters again. He warmed to the possibilities, his mind far away from Kleiser, who jerked him back to reality by stumbling over his feet.

'Where you going?'

But Kleiser neither answered nor looked his way, stooping through the narrow entrance of the cave with his small helmet jammed hard on his head and with strands of reddish hair protruding from beneath its coal-scuttle brim.

Scherfe watched him go.

He evidently planned to find Stumm, probably already windy at the thought of having to make his own decisions.

Across the valley the sky was brightening above the treetops and there were patches of blue sky floating in with the dawn. It looked as though the rain had stopped, but the entrance of the cave up to the spot where Stumm had slept was still running water.

But Scherfe didn't stir. Suppose Kleiser hadn't gone looking for Stumm and had snatched at a sudden chance of escape — just as he'd been thinking? Then things couldn't be better! Kleiser's desertion would make it all the easier for him. All he need do now was hang on where he was. If American patrols came down the valley it didn't matter a damn. He'd no intention of carrying on a personal war. And if any of their scouts happened to stumble into this cave, then all he had to do was put his hands up.

'*Kamarad! Alles kaput!*'

A quarter of an hour passed. Half an hour. A full hour.

Scherfe lay back on his haversack telling himself that for him the war was as good as over. Suddenly, the slosh-slosh of heavy boots over waterlogged ground warned him of somebody approaching.

Jackboots!

German boots!

Probably Helmut Kleiser, who'd given up hope of finding Stumm and hadn't the initiative to find himself some place to lie low. Scherfe's lip curled at the feeble-mindedness of the man.

But it wasn't Kleiser who was standing framed in the narrow opening but the tall, lean body of Klaus Stumm. The sturmann peered into the cave.

'Where's Kleiser?'

The words sharp as pistol shots.

Scherfe's face stiffened and he found himself pressing his back hard against the stone. If Stumm had come back with murder in his heart then there wasn't a thing he could do to help himself. His Schmeiser was a good metre away. Even his kommando knife was sheathed to his haversack behind him.

'He went out looking for you, sturmann!'

Stumm grinned

'An' how about you, Scherfe? Why didn't you come looking? Maybe you were thinking your sturmann had deserted his section, huh?'

Scherfe shook his head trying to relax, to appear convincing.

'I stayed here because I expected you back.'

Stumm gave him that same grin again.

'That's quick thinking.' he said. 'Kleiser wouldn't have been so bright, would he?'

Scherfe didn't answer as he watched Stumm come into the cave. He was thinking what his chances were of turning over on to his back and making a haphazard snatch at his kommando knife. If Stumm became violent that might be the only chance he'd have to survive.

Stumm came deeper into the cave and eased the MG-42 off his shoulder, leaning it against the stone wall balanced on its butt-plate, then squatting on his haunches facing Scherfe.

Scherfe shifted uneasily, conscious of those fierce blue eyes drilling into his own. He wanted to say something to break the spell of that close scrutiny, but he held his tongue, scared of sending Stumm flying off the handle.

'Did I frighten you last night, Scherfe?'

Scherfe's young face hardened and he swallowed in a dry throat. He'd a feeling that Stumm was playing with him. The cat and mouse game of a demented mind.

'Well?'

Scherfe shrugged, shaking his head at the same time.

'You had a nightmare, that was all!'

'A nightmare you call it?'

'That's what it looked like to me, sturmann.'

Stumm gave him that pitying grin again and then went off at a tangent.

'Have you any idea what's over the ridge to the south?'

Scherfe, having trouble in switching his line of thought at that speed, shook his head.

Stumm said, 'Nobody troubled to find out, did they?'

'No, sturmann. Not yet.'

'Not yet? How much time d'you think we've got in this bloody war? You an' that thick-headed farmer's boy! Or were you gambling on me whooping off down the valley like some lunatic? Maybe I did frighten you last night! Eh? I'd say you were planning to see the war through in this bloody cave. Kleiser an' you! Christ! What a pair you'd make!'

Scherfe's eyes never left Stumm's face, half-expecting to see foam bubbling from his lips. But, in contrast, it appeared that much of the tension of the past few days had left him. Could it be that the convulsions of the night, sparked off by the death of Franz Kreutzmann, had done something to help Stumm's mental stability?

He snatched at the possibility.

'I'd have done a recce this morning, sturmann,' he said. 'I realise we need to know what's over the lip of the hill.'

'Then what'd you expect to find?'

Scherfe took a chance.

'A railway line?'

Unexpectedly, Stumm stood up and strode vigorously back to the mouth of the cave, his helmet hanging by its chin-strap from the fingers of his left hand, his fair hair blowing in the breeze, eyes slitted against the climbing sun. He appeared to have become suddenly bored with ribbing Scherfe and, from Scherfe's point of view, so far as he could remember this was about the most he'd ever heard the sturmann say at any one time.

Seconds passed whilst Stumm continued to scan the rising woodland across the valley. Then he half-turned, speaking

over his shoulder with eyes still focused on the distant land-
scape.

'Yeh! That's right, Scherfe. There's a railway line. The line
from Robichon-sur-Florentin.'

Scherfe took in a deep breath. The day wasn't going at all as
he'd hoped. The railway line from Robichon-sur-Florentin
hadn't had any place in his plans to see the war through in
hiding. Now it seemed that Stumm could be contemplating
rejoining the battle for Normandy. His eyes clamped upon
Stumm's lean body, concentrated on the spot between his
shoulder blades where the leather braces of his equipment
crossed.

An aiming disc!

He found his right hand creeping over the dusty floor to
where his Schmeiser machine pistol lay with a magazine
already clipped, a round in the chamber and the mechanism
cocked. One dive and there was a chance he could fire a burst
into Stumm's unprotected back. Right there where the braces
crossed. That way he would be free of Stumm and also free of
the war. As easy as that!

Or was it so easy?

There could be no telling whether Stumm had set himself up
for such a possibility – probably with the butt of his Luger
already clasped in the hand inside his steel helmet!

There also came into Scherfe's leaping mind the inevitable
images of his home and his mother, as they always did at times
of great personal tension. But then Stumm turned to face him
with that same pitying half-smile, as though the bastard had
known all along what was going through his mind. Scherfe
knew he'd missed whatever chance of escape he'd had.

He made a show of stretching himself and clambering to his
feet.

'Permission to ask a question, sturmann?'

Stumm turned again to the distant hillside.

'Like what?'

'Are we planning to move east along the railway line?'

But Stumm didn't reply immediately, and when he did what
he said had nothing to do with his plans for the day.

'Lash the spare barrel back into your pack straps,' he said
harshly, 'from now on you're Number Two on the Spandau!'

Helmut Kleiser joined them five minutes later. From the
mouth of the cave Stumm and Scherfe watched him climbing
laboriously from the foot of the valley over the rough outcrop.
It was clear that the man was lost for he halted frequently,

shielding his eyes from the sun to view the length of the escarpment.

Stumm picked up the MG-42 and clipped in the half-full ammunition belt, then meticulously adjusted the strap over his right shoulder. Scherfe watched him with interest as he buckled on his own equipment. He wondered if thoughts were going through Stumm's mind about Kleiser close to those which, a few minutes earlier, had been going through his own mind about Stumm.

But as they emerged from the cave into the sunlight, Kleiser spotted them. He halted abruptly, waving, and as they moved across the valley he had to run so that when eventually he caught up with them he was blowing hard and streaming sweat.

He fell into line behind Scherfe without comment. It was clear that this was just another day to Helmut Kleiser and whatever had gone before had probably already drained from his memory.

Stumm led them over the hill to the south with the noise of battle all around them. It was as though the two great armies, refreshed after the night's storm, had been over-eager to resume their killing and destruction.

But the valley through which Stumm and his section marched was clear of soldiers. This was a difficult stretch of ground, impassable to tanks and armoured vehicles and too insignificant strategically to involve their hard-pressed infantry.

Beyond the crest of the hill a panorama of smoothly undulating agricultural land stretched endlessly before them. It looked green and lush after the night's downpour, with a thin haze beginning to rise from the lower ground under a warming sun.

Here, on the higher ground, there were also visible signs of battle: intermittent muzzle flashes of medium artillery, at that distance impossible to categorise as battery or self-propelled. The flat burst of their shells could also be spotted, grey mushrooms of soil which suddenly spurted in and amongst the hedgerows and the strips of woodland which screened areas of dead ground. Only the irritable rattle of machine guns and the sporadic crackle of rifle fire indicated the rising impatience of both armies.

Stumm's section halted a hundred metres or so down the reverse slope. Stumm motioned them into cover in the long grass and eased the MG-42 off his shoulder, squatting on his haunches and scanning the panorama leisurely through binoculars from east to west, as though the topography was already imprinted on his mind.

He handed them to Rudi Scherfe.

Scherfe knew what Stumm expected him to define – the Robichon-sur-Florentin/St Jouin railway. He ranged the binoculars into the middle distance as Stumm had done, hoping to Christ he'd spot the narrow-gauge line. But before he'd completed his first traverse it sprang into his vision – a straight stretch of glittering steel maybe four kilometres distant.

He focused meticulously until the two converging lines became needle-sharp.

'The railway line, sturmann!'

It was more of a statement than a question and Scherfe kept the binoculars to his eyes, describing the surrounding topography as he'd heard Kreutzmann and Stumm himself do over the past weeks.

'Line about four kilometres ahead! No sign of movement along its length. Line straight east to west within field of vision. Seems undamaged. No sign of any troop movement in vicinity. Line disappears into woodland maybe three kilometres farther east. Sturmann!'

Stumm stuck out a hand and Scherfe put the binoculars into the outstretched fingers, but when he caught Kleiser's eye he recognised a sneer of contempt in the big man's expression. Kleiser clearly didn't fancy a role subordinate to a schoolboy and Scherfe guessed that Kleiser believed he'd used the time in the cave with Stumm to angle himself the Number Two position on the MG-42 machine gun.

This wasn't something Scherfe welcomed. He'd a big enough problem keeping an eye on Stumm without having to think about Kleiser shooting him in the back in a churlish fit of pique. There'd always been something mean and vicious about Kleiser's nature which, without warning, could suddenly erupt through the fog of the man's animal mind. It was a dicey situation being a part of a trio in which murder could as easily spring from within as from the common enemy.

'We'll take us a look!'

Stumm got to his feet as he spoke, clipping the MG-42 back on to its sling as he strode forcefully down the hill without waiting for the other two to follow. He was making no effort to use cover, hurrying over the tufted grass as though the

Robichon railway had suddenly developed a special significance.

But a few hundred metres short of the track he halted abruptly, again reaching for his binoculars. Scherfe and Kleiser screwed their eyes against the sun, also following the length of line.

'Smoke, sturmann!'

This from Kleiser, standing farther up the hillside and pointing eastwards into the hazy middle distance.

Stumm nodded.

'Yeh, smoke.'

And he left it at that, slipping the binoculars back into the pouch at his belt and shouldering the MG-42 in his effortless way.

Scherfe and Kleiser again dropped into single file behind him, moving due east over the angle of the hill and parallel to the line.

As they closed the distance the rising column of blue-grey smoke sharpened against the sky above the horizon. Then they moved into more woodland, temporarily losing sight of the railway. But when they once again cleared the trees with the soothing odour of woodsmoke there also came an acrid stench of high-explosive and the sickly, sweet smell of death.

On impulse Scherfe turned to Kleiser, marching stolidly behind him, and it was apparent from the way the big man was sniffing the air that he was having similar reactions. As he met Scherfe's questioning glance he shook his head. He'd no idea, either, what was happening along that railway track and, for once, he was bright enough to realise that neither had Stumm. Whatever it was their section leader was seeking had nothing to do with a railway.

As the line disappeared into what appeared to be a cutting through yellow stone outcrop, Stumm unpredictably changed direction and headed towards it.

Now the stench of death was all about them, the air was heavy with putrefaction. Stumm turned his head, seeking their reactions and, as he did so, he stumbled over a bloody object half-buried in the grass. Scherfe, behind him, caught his step. It was a human leg which had been severed halfway above the knee, still wearing a ragged fringe of field grey uniform above the German jackboot. The blackened, blood-encrusted stump through which a few centimetres of shattered bone protruded was already breeding maggots; their short fat bodies rippling in a yellow jelly as they bored deeper into the dead flesh.

Stumm waved them into line-abreast: Scherfe to the left, Kleiser to the right. And in that makeshift formation they closed the distance to the line of outcrop which marked the rim of the cutting.

They came upon more lumps of human bodies, many of them also with scraps of uniform embedded into the bloody gobbets of flesh. An arm still wearing a wristwatch, its dial shattered and leather strap blackened with a soaking of blood which had caked the arm and fingernails. Half a head, incongruously wedged into what remained of a coal-scuttle helmet, the one remaining eye opaque, glazed and distant in its hollow socket; the other side of the face a mangled unrecognisable mess which looked as though a purée of blackberries had been mashed into the helmet. A corpse close to the rim of the cutting which appeared to have no bones and which had crumpled like a discarded puppet into an impossible attitude. There was no sign of wounds on it, but a wide pool of dried blood which stained the grass around it indicated there could be terrible injuries beneath it, as if some gigantic force had nonchalantly tossed it clear of the railway line.

Stumm looked down at it contemplatively, lifting an epaulette with the toe of his boot and Scherfe, too, recognised an insignia identical to that of the two dead Waffen SS panzergrenadiers they'd found at the scene of the Robichon massacre.

Now they knew what was down there. The Americans — or somebody — had ambushed the train and the panzergrenadiers had been annihilated to a man. Otherwise, why were there none about, seeing to their dead?

Stumm glanced wryly at Scherfe, then briefly indicated a route back up the hillside.

Scherfe nodded his understanding. There was no point in climbing down to the line. It no longer mattered a damn who'd blown up the train and it was too late to seek reprisals. To the boy's way of thinking, the Waffen SS had got what they deserved. Rough justice had been done and somewhere down there amongst the death and destruction would be the shattered corpses of the officers who'd condoned the brutal killing of women and children. Serve the murdering bastards right — even if they were German!

Now they were again marching at a steady pace and less than a hundred metres north of the railway line, moving towards more woodland. Stumm seemed unusually relaxed as though he'd attained some degree of personal fulfilment by

116

finding the ambush and now had time to spare. If only the bloody man would talk now and then, Scherfe thought.

Behind him Helmut Kleiser, like Stumm, seemed to be enjoying this march from which the usual dangers of ambush, mortar fire and pot-shotting Yank snipers had miraculously vanished.

If only it had been Kleiser who'd been knocked off during yesterday's battle instead of Kreutzmann, Scherfe pondered. For, at such times as this, Kreutzmann could usually be relied upon to state an opinion and that was what he needed right now. There was something menacing about this languid dream-like sequence which had unaccountably absorbed the section. Scherfe didn't like it and the nagging memory of Stumm's fits during the night did nothing to help him.

It was as they were entering a deep belt of trees on gently undulating ground that there came a sharp, guttural command.

'Halt!'

Stumm stopped in his tracks, slipping the MG-42 off his shoulder so that the butt-plate rested on the ground beside his right foot, rifle fashion. Behind him, Scherfe and Kleiser shambled to a halt, startled.

Stumm half-turned.

'Drop your weapons!' he ordered in a parade-ground voice loud enough to carry to the trees.

Then, as they dropped their Schmeiser machine pistols, a group of panzergrenadiers emerged silently from cover. These men were operationally equipped, also carrying Schmeisers and with the leather straps of their equipment hung with canvas magazine pouches and dotted with stick grenades. On either flank, MG-42 teams squatted in the grass with their machine guns mounted on their bipods and ammunition belts laced.

Only Helmut Kleiser showed any surprise when he recognised the burly form of Unterscharfuhrer Heinz Boeckh. By this time Scherfe had realised what had been at the back of Stumm's mind ever since they'd left the cave that morning. Without Franz Kreutzmann at his side he was no longer willing to wage a private war against a hotchpotch of Yank infantry intent on keeping them from the Sarthe river. Evidently Stumm had decided that the only way to make a break through a constricting ring of American firepower was with an operational German field detachment.

Rudi Scherfe smiled ruefully to himself as the reason behind the past hour's euphoria struck him.

He recalled sitting in the cave and looking at the spot between Stumm's shoulder blades where the leather straps of his equipment crossed.

If only he'd had the guts ...!

Chapter Seven

It was the fact that Franz Kreutzmann and the unknown Frenchwoman were missing from Sturmann Stumm's MG-42 machine gun section which had finally swayed Obersturmfuhrer Hans Thielker's decision. Even so, he was by no means convinced that Stumm hadn't chickened out of the action during the battle to the south a couple of days earlier and that it had been nothing other than the man's bad luck which had caused him and his section to stumble back upon the detachment.

Stumm had been astute enough to anticipate Thielker's reaction, but this was also a development on which he'd had time to speculate. His toneless explanation to an angry Thielker, who at the back of his mind was already lining up a firing squad, was simple and short enough to be credible.

'We were cut off on the left flank by Browning machine guns, Herr Obersturmfuhrer! We tried to fight our way back, but both my Number Two and the Frenchwoman were killed. When we got short on ammo I decided to lie low until we could rejoin your detachment!'

That was all. Enough. And he made a gesture of pointing out the empty Schmeiser ammunition pouches and the half-loaded belts for the MG-42. Scherfe helped by dragging round his left trouser leg and showing the shrapnel slice across his thigh.

Even so, Thielker wasn't convinced and there returned to him the same doubts he'd had when he'd first looked over Stumm's tall and rangy figure, the pale blue eyes set in the haggard face with its week's growth of beard. There was also the same wildness about the three survivors which went some way towards discrediting what could be a true and logical explanation.

Yet, after all, the dark-haired ill-looking man – Stumm's pal – had died . . .

'Very well!' Thielker decided abruptly. 'Unterscharfuhrer Boeckh will allocate you to a platoon.'

It was the same old problem, Thielker decided as he turned

on his heel towards his makeshift headquarters in a slit-trench geometrically sited in the centre of the triangle angled by his three machine gun sections. The detachment was too thin on the ground to execute seasoned grenadiers on mere hunches. But he'd make bloody sure that Sturmann Klaus Stumm and his two cronies were kept under close observation during their next action together!

In the two days since Obersturmfuhrer Hans Thielker's detachment had disengaged from the American ambush, it had become apparent to him that Oberkommando Wehrmacht was taking new and positive steps to see that the fast-moving spearheads of the US 3rd Army did not have everything their own way.

Prior to his forced march to the railway cutting where he had found the Waffen SS not only dead but obliterated, he had watched through binoculars freshly-equipped Wehrmacht infantry feeling their way westwards in some strength, evidently to form a chain of defensive strongpoints across the supply and support lines of the US reconnaisance battle groups.

This unexpected sight had cheered him and he had spent time patiently briefing his battle-weary detachment on further positive involvement. Later, he had tuned his solitary field R/T set to the panzer frequency and, despite their codes, had recognised several Russian-experienced units new to the Normandy battlefront.

It was during the morning following the return of Stumm's machine gun section that Theilker came upon units of a reinforcement battle group moving in a direction contrary to that of the main body of the Wehrmacht — from east to west!

It had been Rottenfuhrer Gunter Eiser's forward scouts who had recognised the swift Panzer Mk V Panthers roaring across country towards them, each with its complement of panzergrenadiers aboard.

Impulsively they had raised their weapons above their heads, cheering at the tops of their voices, recognising in the Panthers an end to the Wehrmacht's demoralised withdrawal from Normandy. Then, as the troop rapidly deployed into line-abreast formation, their expressions changed, but they bravely held their ground frantically signalling a warning back to Eiser. If the Panther formation had mistaken them for Americans then they could expect a burst of Spandau fire in their backs right now!

But Thielker had also interpreted the scouts' signals and had snatched at his binoculars to find that the forward line of panzers had topped the rise before he'd had time to put them to his eyes. He was as quick to recognise the danger as Eiser's section had been. Operational panzers, swanning loose across enemy-held territory, would be expecting to bump into only enemy – not a nameless hotchpotch of German infantry gathered from a score of different regiments.

Thielker fired his Kampfpistole into the air as the first salvo of HE shells tore through the trees above him, over-ranged, and exploded in the undergrowth a hundred metres behind their positions. But as the red flare blossomed and began to stream back to earth, the Panthers cut their speed and the turret gunners relaxed at their weapons. The leading panzer churned to a halt close to where the two scouts had dived at the blast of the 75s.

At that point, Eiser and the four grenadiers of his rifle section broke cover, leaving their supporting MG-42 machine gun at a flank. Eiser wasn't happy with the unannounced arrival of reinforcements and recalled rumours of American tank men rigged out in German uniforms and riding salvaged panzers.

Thielker also watched these developments uneasily, but when he saw Eiser and his six men climb aboard the command panzer he strode out into the meadow, while the remaining four Panthers raced away to seek hull-down positions in an all-round defence pattern along the bocage hedges. He was quick to spot the divisional insignia stencilled immediately below the long barrel of the command Panther's 75mm gun. It was one he found easy to recognise: 10th Panzer Division, 'Frundsberg'.

He'd had the impression that the Frundsberg Division had been operating in the Mortain region in a support role after recently being released from its tactical laager east of the Seine. He shrugged negatively at this unexpected encounter. The Frundsberg had not been mustered until 1942 when it had performed garrison duties in the Marseilles region before being sent to the Russian front. There it had served in Tarnapol and in the northern Ukraine, before being rushed into tactical reserve as soon as Oberkommando Wehrmacht had given credence to the establishment of Allied beachheads on the Contentin peninsula of Normandy.

Earlier, Thielker recalled, there had been rumours that the division was being detached from the Mortain front to concentrate on the defence of the Wehrmacht's southern flank. This explained the arrival of these forward elements, evidently operating in a reconnaissance role but without scout cars.

A young-looking untersturmfuhrer was climbing out of the command panzer and as it slowed to a standstill he vaulted easily from the track guard. He strode vigorously to Thielker, snapped to attention and saluted.

There was a hint of humour in his expression.

'Herr Obersturmfuhrer! You surprised us. We didn't expect to find panzergrenadiers on this axis.' Then 'Untersturmfuhrer Rudiger Seigen, 10th SS Panzers.'

'Lucky for us you over-ranged, Seigen!'

Seigen nodded, willing to accept criticism for his impulse, but at the same time anxious to make the point that accuracy with a ranging salvo couldn't be guaranteed from a Panther moving fast over undulating ground.

He said wryly: 'You look as though you've had a rough time, Obersturmfuhrer,' his eyes wandering over the ragged, battle-stained uniforms of Eiser's section as the men climbed down from the panther. He asked, 'Is this the whole of your force?'

Thielker half-turned, calling over his shoulder to Heinz Boeckh to bring out the rest of the grenadiers from their foxholes, including the wounded.

Seigen's eyebrows lifted as they emerged from the screen of woodland: three NCOs – Boeckh, Zimmermann and Stumm – followed by nineteen grenadiers. Four of the fit men had fallen during the ambush in the forest and two of the wounded had died from further injuries sustained from random shelling by American mortars.

'About half are from the 2nd Battalion of the 4th Panzergrenadier Regiment of the 12th SS Hitler Youth,' Thielker told him. 'The rest I picked up on the way east.' He pointed to Stumm's MG-42 machine gun section, the sturmann scowling under the close scrutiny, fixing his blue eyes on the Panther officer as though daring him to comment. But Seigen had no intention of criticising the appearance of another officer's troops. Even though he had had little battle experience in the Mortain region, such sorry-looking grenadiers were not new to him. He'd seen the pale remnants of battalions of them all the way south as they'd reeled before the onslaught of the superbly-equipped US 3rd Army and strike-aircraft of the USAAF. He unclipped a canvas-covered map case from his belt and tossed back the flap, turning the marked-up talc overprint to Thielker.

He prodded a forefinger at a series of red hieroglyphics, orientating the map to the ground so that the contour lines conformed to a long range of hills farther to the south.

'That's roughly the area we're making for,' he said. 'On the high ground above the road network you see there.' He shrugged. 'Unfortunately, we've no Intelligence on the American commitment, but understand it dominates one of their lines of axis.'

'Surely you're not telling me you plan to intercept with five Panthers?' Thielker smiled. 'You should know that the Yanks burn up these roads with a full regiment of armour at a time!'

Seigen shook his head, also smiling.

'Just so, Herr Obersturmfuhrer. Our tactics at this stage are chosen with tactical withdrawal in mind. Probably a series of swift attacks rather than a major setpiece manoeuvre. But now that reinforcements are coming west in strength we're getting much stronger behind. Trouble is the damned American bombers and fighter-bombers. The bastards are hammering our spearheads and bogging down reinforcements.'

Ten minutes later, Thielker watched the five Panthers head south-east in the direction which Seigen had indicated on his map. From where they were standing they couldn't see the road network which was to be the panzers' ultimate objective, but that was none of their responsibility.

Even so, the unexpected arrival of the Frundsberg Division into this theatre of operations had lifted Thielker's morale. Seigen had radioed back to the officer commanding the division, Standartenfuhrer Siegfried Alsfeld, that Thielker and his detachment were about to march the sixteen kilometres to join them.

When Thielker told his men the news and indicated the 10th SS Division's laager on his map, the wounded had immediately shied at the distance. But Thielker had convinced them that, from now on, he planned to avoid trouble. Their one and only intention was to reach that laager intact.

This raised a faint cheer from the men and caused Scherfe to go along with Stumm's belief that if ever they were going to make it back to the Fatherland, then they'd have to fight their way there with organised and disciplined troops. In the congestion around the river bridges there wasn't a chance in hell of rag-tag bands of deserters making the crossings.

Thiekler's detachment — including the eight wounded — made the sixteen kilometres to the panzer laager without incident. There had been considerable air activity over the area as

Seigen had warned, but the bombers' targets had been kilo-metres farther east and there had been no signs of either Ameri-can infantry or of wandering bands of leaderless Wehrmacht.

Later that day, the detachment was merged into the highly-operational 10th SS Panzer Division Frundsberg.

Up to that time, the wounded had resigned themselves to violent deaths on the field of battle, incapable of protecting themselves from the Americans or against the deluge of high-explosive which would rain down on them from the sky. During the past weeks they'd seen too many of their mates blown into twisted, mangled coils of blood, sinew and bone. Now, it was barely within their comprehension that they were to be sent to the rear — probably as far back as Germany — where they'd be given civilian hospital treatment. There'd be clean, white sheets, fleecy blankets, spring mattresses and they'd have nothing to do but lie there whilst highly-skilled surgeons and pretty nurses made them whole again.

Couldn't happen, could it?

What? After Normandy? Not a chance! No bugger gave a damn for washed-up grenadiers!

But when they'd been fed and their stomachs were heavy with the richest food they'd tasted in months they were ready to accept that, for them, the war could be over. Long live the Frundsberg and good luck to the cocky bastards! Let them knock hell out of the Yanks! And thanks to Obersturmfuhrer Thielker who'd led them from oblivion and given them a chance to become men again.

The fit men from the detachment were split into groups of four or five and posted to the four companies within the 2nd Battalion. Such procedure was in accord with the scrambling of decimated units. It wasn't considered wise to keep too many old mates together. That way they could form cliques, even within small formations, and that was no good at all when victory and survival frequently depended on team effort.

There was only one group of three and that was Sturmann Klaus Stumm's MG-42 machine gun section. He, Scherfe and Kleiser were posted to No 3 Platoon of No 1 Company under the command of Rottenfuhrer Karl Fiesch, No 2 Section Leader.

As it happened, No 1 Company was in battalion reserve at the time.

As Untersturmfuhrer Rudiger Seigen had said to Hans Thielker, the Frundsberg Division had already run into

124

problems in that Oberkommando Wehrmacht was able to supply but limited Intelligence on the extent of penetration of the American 3rd Army into Eastern Normandy. This meant they had no knowledge of which towns had been captured by them, what strategic points had been taken, or what was the true direction of their main thrust. All they did know for certain was that the German 275th Infantry Division was already dug in somewhere much too far to the north to be of any use.

Consequently, plans had been made by 10th SS Panzer Division Headquarters to establish contact with units of the 275th Division and, meanwhile, attempt to seize road junctions and tactically important land features which could subsequently be occupied by the 275th Division and other mobile infantry units.

This had also turned out to be a tall order, for on the morning that Thielker's detachment was merged into the 2nd Battalion, Untersturmfuhrer Seigen contacted HQ with the information that as far as he could ascertain US spearheads were already up to twenty kilometres east of the line on which the main German northern defences were being established.

Other units subsequently reported that Allied Air Forces had destroyed most of the bridges from the Dives to the Seine. This indicated that reinforcements as well as heavy equipment such as guns and armour would be restricted until German engineers could throw pontoons across these rivers or erect prefabricated bridges.

Even so, the Frundsberg was in no way to be deviated from its original brief which, by way of Oberkommando Wehrmacht, was said to have come direct from Reichsfuhrer Adolf Hitler himself! That order was — *counterattack!*

Two days after joining Fiesch's section, Klaus Stumm and his MG-42 machine gun section found themselves no longer in divisional reserve, but with the spearhead of the new offensive against an axis of the American eastward thrust.

It was on a damp and chilly morning, in sharp contrast to the balmy weather of the past few days, that the 2nd Battalion deployed on to their attack start-line. There was also an eerie stillness to the air, the first grey light of dawn doing little more than tingeing the horizon. Stumm kept himself to himself as he always did in the minutes prior to an attack. He fidgeted with the breech mechanism of the Spandau and hauled the spare barrel from Scherfe's haversack straps to make sure the rifling was clean. But he said little and the three of them moved in

125

single file behind Rottenfuhrer Fiesch's riflemen towards a roadside ditch where the panzergrenadiers were to form up in order of advance, prior to climbing aboard the Mk V Panthers. These were to carry them forward and dump them on the edge of the American infantry positions before they swanned off to seek out the armour.

The brief had been sketchy, for precise operational Intelligence was still lacking and there had been insufficient time for the grenadiers to push forward night patrols to test the strength and depth of the American positions. Even up to this time, minutes before 'H'-hour, the Germans didn't know whether the Americans were expecting a counterattack or not. All they knew for certain was that they'd be standing-to in strength at dawn with armour and infantry, on both northern and southern flanks of their supply corridor.

In the ditch Scherfe squatted on Stumm's right in the gun's Number Two position, Kleiser at the other side.

Scherfe was unusually calm, as though an organised assault with the crack Frundsberg Division had brought back some rationality to his involvement as a panzergrenadier. After months of doubt he was conscious of a strong sense of patriotism, which he put down to the knowledge that his survival no longer lay solely in the hands of Sturmann Klaus Stumm.

Kleiser also seemed more relaxed. He lay flat on his belly with his feet at the bottom of the ditch and his head poking above the grass which lined the verge. There was an expression of quiet acceptance about his now cleanly-shaven face as his eyes followed the contour of the rising ground which was to be a part of their initial objective. The hills were brightening visibly with each passing minute, the greys dissolving into yellows, greens and ochres, a flush of red dawn suddenly warming the blue steel of their freshly oiled weapons.

All remained still. The quiet before the holocaust! No chatter. No clicking of rifle bolts. No banging of mess-tins. No shifting of ammunition belts. They all knew the drill. Soon the barrage would begin and then they could make as much noise as they'd a mind to.

With the first salvo of ranging shots from the 88mm guns of self-propelled 'Jagdpanthers' positioned a couple of kilometres to the rear, there also came the deep-throated surges of power from the forward panzers as their engines sprang to life, spluttering fitfully against condensation.

Scherfe shot a worried glance at Stumm, but he still

appeared to be relaxed, evidently unconcerned at what the day was to bring, prepared to take his chances so long as he was fighting a real war.

The flat blasts of the SP barrage multiplied as shells tore over the panzergrenadiers' positions like express trains, little above treetop level. But they exploded out of sight, somewhere on the reverse slope of the hill in front of them, the gunners firing on trajectory and ranged by observation officers who had gone forward with infantry patrols during the night, prepared to risk their lives under their own bombardment.

Still no counter-fire came from the Americans.

Could it be that the axis line wasn't manned at that point? Could be, but bloody unlikely! Now the SP barrage was thickening, still bracketing targets beyond the forward slope. Officers in full battle gear emerged from the trees at the other side of the road, shouting irritably above the tumult of the shells, motioning the grenadiers to the waiting panzers which, with engines still snorting, had churned themselves into a deployed line-abreast formation, guns trained on the hill ahead.

The grenadiers raced to their pre-allocated panzers and scrambled aboard, huddling behind the turrets, finding reassurance in the fact that the commanders and their drivers hadn't battened down the hatches. It always put the grenadiers' morale down a couple of pegs when they came under enemy fire from three sides and the panzer crews locked themselves in their shell and bullet-proof steel boxes.

Armoured personnel carriers were better! Some were even fitted with armour plate above the grenadiers' heads to shield them from mortar fire and airbursts. But these were becoming things of the past – and their specialist crews! No army liked to see an enemy alive, fit and superbly equipped, deposited bang on their positions before they'd had a chance to recover from the pre-bombardment. Consequently, in the Battle of Normandy, armoured personnel carriers had soon become a priority target for Allied gunners and strafing aircraft, as had the MK VI Tigers themselves.

As the roar of the German barrage rose into a crescendo of shrieking, exploding shrapnel the Panthers began to edge from their positions below the hill. Ahead, there was no cover and the grenadiers clamped hollow-charge bombs into their panzerschreck and panzerfaust anti-tanks weapons on the chance that American armour could be lying in cover beyond the crest. At the same time panzer crews were alerted, the gunners sliding high-velocity, armour-piercing shells into the chambers of their 75mm and 88mm guns.

Meanwhile, panzer commanders sat nonchalantly on the rims of their turrets with earphones and throat microphones fixed, maintaining contact with command panzers and tactical Headquarters.

Halfway up the long slope they reached their point of no return, at this stage anticipating either an artillery/anti-tank pepper-pot barrage or to see squadrons of Sherman tanks bucking out of hull-down positions, in a steam-roller counter-attack to shove them back down the hill. These would probably be supported by an air-strike and the sky would become black with fighter-bombers so that, initially, all the American armour would hope to do was trundle forward into battle and watch the Panthers brew up, one after another! This was a grim prospect and one not new to the 10th SS Panzer Division Frundsberg despite their short experience in this sector of the front.

But as they boosted their throttles against the steepening gradient there was still no sign of American resistance, and they began to wonder if there was some truth in the rumour that General George Patten had over-extended his lines of communication and that the main body of armour and supporting infantry had been unable to keep pace with his fast-moving reconnaissance spearheads.

Maybe the Frundsberg could throw an armoured block astride the axis of the Yank advance and sit there unchallenged until the 275th Infantry Division arrived to take over? That would be great! For each and every respite, no matter how short, gave more time to reinforcements and armour arriving from east of the Seine. But what a hope that was!

Near to the top of the slope the Americans had still not engaged. There, the Panthers deployed into thinly-spaced defensive lines, wary of topping the crest without reconnaissance, knowing there could be enemy anti-tank guns sited wheel to wheel in the trees beyond. So, still on the forward slope, they halted and the grenadiers jumped down and raced forward heedless of their own barrage.

Sturmann Klaus Stumm led his machine gun section parallel to the riflemen, knowing that sooner or later they'd have to take their chances with the American counter-barrage. One of an infantry NCO's problems was deciding where a support barrage ended and the enemy barrage began – or if the two were ranged on to identical targets!

But as the forward platoons reached the crest the German barrage died. It was a ragged affair, with a couple of the SPs still sending over isolated shells after the rest had finished their fireplan.

Seconds later, the first ranging shots of the American counter-fire began to drop. They were intermittent and all of them concentrated on the forward infantry, none attempting to bracket the Panthers below the crest.

Hauptsturmfuhrer Walter Becker, commanding No 1 Company of panzergrenadiers, was quick to appreciate that the Americans hadn't yet realised that there was panzer support. What the hell did they think this was? he asked himself. A daylight infantry patrol? A limited skirmish seeking prisoners?

He grinned at their vulnerability as he grabbed the hand microphone from his signaller and spoke urgently to Tactical Headquarters. Then he motioned his two forward platoons into a line-abreast formation, and they doubled over the crest screaming like banshees, firing their MG-42 machine guns and Schmeiser machine pistols from the hip. In support, the Panthers jolted forward, in and amongst the grenadiers, firing over open sights into the trees and undergrowth down the reverse slope.

Immediately there came sporadic small-arms fire in reply. The bullets were going high, over-ranged, but there were also a couple of Browning heavy machine guns firing very low, daisy-cutting, so that the heads of poppies and cornflowers suddenly sprang from their stalks for no apparent reason. The Brownings were also working together, deeply entrenched, moving in traverses which sprayed the entire grenadier front, causing casualties.

Untersturmfuhrer Konrad Lintz, commanding No 1 Platoon, slowed his pace with the intention of dropping off his MG-42 sections to shoot in a rifleman assault, but the Brownings were too well camouflaged, even their muzzle flashes lost amongst the dense foliage.

Stumm didn't like this either. The first taste of battle and the thrill of joining a spearhead attack with an operational panzer formation began to fade as grenadiers crumpled silently under the withering fire. Some just rolled forward on to their knees and remained in semi-crouching positions as though they were patiently waiting for the order to resume the advance. Others dropped screaming to the grass as the daisy-cutting Brownings mashed their feet and ankles into a bloody pulp. Then, as they floundered helplessly on their stomachs, the same cone of fire got them in the head. The force of the heavy-calibre bullets pitched away their helmets, their scalps and most of their faces leaving a red-streaming mess of sinew, muscles and brains which spilled copiously over the threshing limbs.

Rudi Scherfe paled as the tempo of killing increased, for he'd had sufficient experience of German assault tactics to know that the support companies wouldn't be committed until the strike company had established its initial objective.

He turned questioningly to Stumm, but the sturmann's expression told him nothing. He seemed remote, as though he were back with the Grossdeutschland Division, ready and waiting for Christ knows what!

There were casualties amongst Fiesch's rifle section to the right. One grenadier caught the full burst of one of the Brownings as it paused before swinging back on its traverse and the bullets ripped open his stomach. Incredibly, he kept on running with his rifle and bayonet pushed out in front of him whilst blood bucketed out of the gaping slip across his waist. He didn't seem to realise he'd been hit and, even when he crashed to the ground with his blood spurting and bubbling over his legs, he tried to burrow himself into a firing position. Then the rest of the assault line was past him, leaving more than a third of its strength lying dead or wounded along the hundred metres they'd covered from the crest.

Still they ran, seeking out the Brownings, already realising they were being sacrificed for a couple of Yank machine guns. Hauptsturmfuhrer Walter Becker had been on the point of ordering his company into cover when the second wave of panzers engaged. The roar of their engines hit the panzergrenadiers like the sound of avenging thunder as the panzers topped the crest at full throttle, churning over the soft ground with their turret MG-42s manned by commanders and their 75mm cannons blasting over open sights into the woodland ahead. Ringing cheers burst from the grenadiers as they zig-zagged through their thinning ranks and they ran behind them, screened by their bulk. Seconds later the two Brownings spluttered into silence and the sharp cries of wounded men rose from the trees. At the first sign of drawing blood the grenadiers increased their pace, the riflemen eager to sink their bayonets into the soft bodies of the enemy infantry.

It soon became evident that the Frundsberg were hitting the Americans with a force the latter hadn't anticipated and, more important, before they'd had time to deploy their armour into a defensive battle formation.

As the first wave of grenadiers raced close behind their Panthers so the second wave crested the hill, now free from the traversing Browning fire as they over-ran the dead and dying of the first wave. Somewhere to the rear of the American positions a couple of heavy mortars began to thud, their bombs pitched short of the crest; but this was a half-hearted attempt at defensive fire, most of them exploding harmlessly astride the start-line from which the second wave's attack had sprung.

By this time the second wave of Panthers had also topped the hill, moving much faster than the strike wave and anxious to consolidate on the American positions before the enemy could summon air-strikes or an armoured counterattack.

These were sound tactics on the part of Standartenfuhrer Siegfried Alsfeld, who had calculated that the preservation of this strip of road was primarily more important to the Americans than inflicting casualties on panzergrenadiers. The road could be re-taken later and when that happened it had to be passable for the weight of US armour, artillery, infantry, and supply vehicles pushing east along its length.

The grenadiers stormed into the American infantry before they could get their heavier weapons out of their foxholes, their banshee battlecries making the early morning hideous with the crash and jar of exploding stick grenades, the clatter of heavy machine guns, the prrt-prrt-prrt of Spandaus and the brisk hammer of their Schmeisers.

The Americans fell back according to plan, seeing nothing to be gained in a bayonet and entrenching tool skirmish. Even so, their casualties mounted before the ferocity of the panzergrenadiers, their dead piling around their slit-trenches, their anti-tank and machine gun emplacements.

Soon, the grenadiers' battlecries began to harden into shouts of exultation. Victory was theirs! The men who'd fallen during the first phase of the attack had not been sacrificed in vain. Now the hard tarmac of the road surface was ringing beneath their jackboots and then they were across, charging headlong after the Americans, seeking to kill, to maim, to avenge their dead.

Klaus Stumm was with the vanguard of the rout, the MG-42 slung from his shoulder and the loose end of the ammunition belt jerking intermittently as he fired random short bursts, conserving ammunition because there wasn't time to clip in a new belt. Rudi Scherfe was at his side, using his Schmeiser machine pistol with an aggression that matched Stumm's. Beyond,

Helmut Kleiser had slung his Schmeiser over his shoulder and was tearing into the American infantry with rifle and bayonet, using the butt as much as the blade, his huge figure towering in the melée of the hand-to-hand fighting, leaving a heap of screaming bodies writhing on the ground behind him.

Now the American withdrawal had neared the cover of the trees which fringed the rising ground south of the road and the Frundsberg armour left the chase to the grenadiers, one company running into near hull-down positions at the point from which the battle had developed. The other two deployed along the road in eastern and western directions, effectively cutting off support to the Americans from their supply route.

To Siegfried Alsfeld the battle had progressed like a copybook, sandtable exercise. In one almighty blitz the Americans had been driven out of their positions, and one of their main arterial supply lines had been effectively severed and would now be held by Frundsberg until the 275th Infantry Division arrived to take over. Furthermore, casualties had been minimal considering the tactical and strategical gains.

He was reaching out a hand to take up the radio handset to pass on his good news to Division HQ when a flurry of explosions came from directly ahead. His driver, long experienced in panzer warfare, switched direction heading for cover, but Alsdorf spun round in his turret with binoculars to his eyes. He had time to see the first wave of his panzergrenadiers, breathless and tiring after their long assault, come face to face with a squadron of American self-propelled guns which opened fire on them over open sights.

To a man the grenadiers went to ground, scraping desperately in the woodland soil as high-explosive shells struck the trees, sending jagged chunks of shrapnel spinning around them with the lethal power of airbursts.

Haupsturmfuhrer Walter Becker, up front with his spearhead, immediately fired a violet signal flare, indicating to his supporting artillery that his company had come under direct armoured attack.

The Panthers also roared into action, hatches battened down as they broke from their makeshift cover to contain the new threat. The result was devastating, for the American self-propelled guns did not have the weight of armour to withstand accurate fire from the Panthers' 75mm and 88mm guns. Within minutes, rising columns of smoke began to dot the hillside as the SPs were destroyed.

The panzergrenadiers began to move forward again, eager

to drive home their assault. Even so, now they moved warily, instinctively seeking cover as they advanced against a thickening concentration of small-arms fire. But by this time the forward Panther Company had caught up with them and began brewing up more US self-propelled guns, as well as directing defensive fire into clumps of undergrowth which could conceal Brownings and mortars.

Whilst it had become apparent to the Frundsberg commanders that the Americans were yielding up their positions along the southern flank of the road, they realised that their battle was by no means won. Now the Americans could be regrouping and planning to hammer the grenadiers with high-explosive until they became too thin on the ground to resist a *coup-de-grâce* which would decimate both them and their armour!

It was now! Right now, after they'd taken the all-important first bite at the US defences that they needed to consolidate in strength. They held a fair-sized chunk of a main axis of the US 3rd Army's advance and the longer they could hang on to it the weaker would be the enemy's pressure on the main German defence line farther east.

American medium and heavy artillery began to pitch into the battle, cleanly avoiding the road as though a pathway fifty metres wide had inexplicably become immune to shellfire. Such accurate ranging was being guided and both grenadier and panzer commanders began to comb commanding high points in an attempt to spot where the US gunnery officers could be sited. But that wasn't easy, even in a sparsely wooded terrain, and they radioed Divisional HQ demanding immediate counter-battery fire on the US medium and heavies. But the shelling increased sufficiently in tempo to contain most of the German batteries. And, even as the Panthers squirmed into hull-down positions in an attempt to cover both flanks of the grenadiers' attack, so more American shellfire came down on to those same flanks. Thus the Frundsberg became contained on three sides by a crippling box barrage as high-explosive began to blast the grenadiers and at the same time pin down the panzers. Ahead, unknown reserves of American infantry and armour were dug in and waiting for the command to counterattack.

Klaus Stumm, lying flat on his belly and impatient for the bombardment to lift, glanced speculatively at Kleiser. Kleiser, with his face bright red and polished with sweat from his exertions, and with his helmet still perched grotesquely on top of his great head returned the sturmann's gaze balefully, unperturbed. Kleiser had taken part in grenadier assaults against armour more than once and this time they'd got Panthers in support, anyway. Besides, the Frundsberg was a crack SS division and would knock hell out of the Yanks once the artillery re-ranged and they could push forward again.

Then, for no reason, he pointed to a tattered bundle of rags lying soaked with blood in the undergrowth a few metres to his left. Stumm followed the line of the pointing finger and recognised the body of Rottenfuhrer Gunther Eiser who'd been a section leader in Thielker's detachment.

Rudi Scherfe also recognised the mangled corpse and much of his earlier confidence began to ebb. The plain fact was that men got killed in every battle – no matter what they'd been through! Eiser had survived three months' fighting in Normandy before he'd found Thielker. He'd also been first on the scene at the massacre at the Robichon halt. And for what? To die on this bloody hillside with half the American Army on the other side? And bloody waiting to blast the guts out of every German who came within range! But when he caught Stumm's eye he did his best to shrug indifference. He was committed and that was all there was to it. Nothing had changed. He was committed!

As he turned back to face front a Panther suddenly brewed up a short distance ahead. One second it was rumbling forward, its 75mm gun blasting a patch of undergrowth some hundred and fifty metres to a flank where a heavy machine gun was dug in, hosing tracer around a group of panzergrenadiers pinned beneath the trees. The next, it was a mushrooming fireball. Its commander caught the full blast which roared from the turret as though a furnace door had been flung open. He stiffened, suddenly and grotesquely, his hands still clasping the turret rim. Then he withered into a black charred stick through which the bones glowed with a bright incandescence, until he collapsed into nothing as though this had not been a man at all.

At the first gush of flame the panzer driver had thrown open his hatch cover, momentarily immune in his forward compartment. He prised himself up from his seat forward of the still-roaring engine and leapt to the ground to stand helplessly by the blazing vehicle. His face froze in horror as he saw his commander burn and then he turned to run frantically towards the American machine guns as though the real threat was behind him and not in front.

One of the guns caught up with him at the end of its traverse and the force of its cone of fire tossed him high into the air, arms flailing above his head before he crashed to the ground, torrenting blood.

Standartenfuhrer Siegfried Alsfeld, sitting high in the turret of his command Panther, without helmet, earphones clamped over his thinning hair, had problems. His head was bent and brow creased as he attempted to interpret the signals coming over the air thick and fast. His immediate problem was that the Americans had begun to jam the frequency. Bastards! They never missed a trick! Also, for the first time since the launch of the attack he was beginning to sense doubt. Up to the point of the box barrage the Frundsberg had been on the way to a quick victory. Now he wasn't so sure. True, they'd captured their main objective. That strip of road was firmly in German hands, but for how long? Were the Yanks intent on turning it into another killing ground? Using it as a heaven-sent chance to annihilate a couple of battalions of the famed Frundsberg?

Could be. Too true it could be!

The Panthers and their grenadiers had gone into the attack according to plan and the Yanks hadn't been standing-to and waiting for them. The trap had come only with their bloody box barrage! Now there wasn't a chance in hell of help from German support units or from the 275th Infantry Division whose fight this was, anyway! Nor could there be much counter-battery fire, simply because the Wehrmacht didn't have more artillery to thicken their barrage, and what they did have was immobilised because there were neither quads nor fuel to shift it to better locations.

Alsfeld took a deep breath as he lifted his head and glimpsed the forward platoons of grenadiers, now gone to ground, returning the Browning fire with MG-42 machine guns and rifles. To the flanks the Panthers had scrambled into whatever positions they'd been able to find in a hurry and were maintaining a steady rate of fire from all their weapons. But that couldn't last! Ammunition was already running low and so long as the box barrage maintained its intensity there were no means of getting more. It could only be a matter of time before the American Shermans, with their Firefly 17-pounder anti-tank guns, came rumbling over the forward slope to knock off the Panthers systematically, one at a time.

After their initial hit-and-miss defensive plan, the Americans had soon learned to be more patient. They would take their time until the Panthers were burning, and then they'd throw in their Calliopes which, in addition to 75mm guns, also carried launching racks for sixty 107mm rockets with which they'd decimate whatever remnants of the panzergrenadier battalions attempted to carry on the fight.

Christ!

Alsfeld hit the rim of the turret hard with the palm of his hand. How could they have been so bloody stupid? Why hadn't some bastard up at Oberkommando Wehrmacht gone out of his way to get them some sort of Intelligence before authorising an attack of this scale?

His lean face drained of colour as a new sound boomed above the battlefield.

Aircraft!

Bloody aircraft!

He lifted his eyes to the sound as the first squadron of P-47 Thunderbolt fighter-bombers of the USAAF hurtled down from four-thousand feet, engines screaming above the thunder of the artillery. Madmen in mad machines intent only on German annihilation! The sky black with the bastards!

At once the American gunners cut the leading edge of the barrage, wary of hitting their own aircraft as they pulled out of their strafing runs.

From the ground there came frenzied cries of 'Napalm!' and at the warning the MG-42s ceased their chatter and the rifle-fire stuttered to a ragged end. But the first sticks of 250lb bombs dropped well wide of their targets and the fireballs raced across the grenadiers' front to explode harmlessly on open ground. Immediately, the grass began to blaze and dense columns of smoke were caught by the wind to billow over the American positions.

To seasoned grenadiers like Klaus Stumm, this sudden turning of the German attack came as an ominous revelation. Along the Eastern Front there'd been many battles in which German divisions had faced far stronger and better equipped Russian units; but these had in no way matched the overwhelming firepower of tanks and aircraft which the Americans had on call.

At the same time, panzer commanders were no longer asking themselves how they were going to consolidate their initial gains, but how they were to extricate two battalions from this holocaust.

Alsfeld provided an answer as the napalm, more accurate now, spurted and flamed across the battlefield. He calmly watched casualties mount up as men turned into living torches while they tried to beat the searing fluid from their bodies with hands which shrivelled on contact.

On Alsfeld's command, the reserve Panther companies churned from their hull-down positions and zig-zagged amongst the grenadiers, who scrambled aboard heedless of the weight of American machine gun fire. Those who were hit were dragged aboard by others whilst the panzers accelerated down the slope and across the road which had been their prime objective.

It was at that point in the battle that the Americans put down the fourth side of their box barrage.

Remnants of the two grenadier battalions consolidated north of the road in an all-round defence formation in which the Panthers became pillboxes and strongpoints, sited strategically with infantry manning support machine guns and anti-tank weapons.

Tactically, the formation was as well positioned here as it had been on the slopes south of the road for the main weight of armament still dominated the American axis. Reports from despatch riders who had braved enemy snipers told of considerable chaos farther west, where American armour and supply vehicles were halted bumper to bumper. These were being shelled by Frundsberg SP artillery and by Jagdpathers equipped with 88mm tank-destroying guns. Heavy casualties were being inflicted amongst men and vehicles, for the American column was unable to deploy over verges softened by the recent rains.

Even so, the condition of the 1st and 2nd Panzergrenadier Battalions was not good. Both had suffered heavy losses during a withdrawal which, for some time, had looked more like a rout. But, on the other hand, their northern flank was still open and limited reinforcements were being fed through the American barrage, whilst the badly wounded were taken to regimental aid posts and field dressing stations.

This information heartened the grenadiers who knew they would soon have to renew the offensive.

The Americans knew it too, and began to concentrate their heavy batteries on to the grenadiers' positions, shelling without interference — for most of them were out of range of the German SP guns and there was no chance of help from the depleted Luftwaffe. But, at the same time, Frundsberg SPs were scouring the likely forming up areas for American infantry in a series of defensive fire tasks hurriedly prepared by forward observation officers up front with infantry patrols.

In No 2 Platoon of No 1 Company, Klaus Stumm and his

section had survived the initial battle, but not without incident. Helmut Kleiser had caught a burst of incendiary bullets which had shredded the left sleeve of his tunic into bloody rags and left a series of parallel weals across his biceps. One of them had burrowed deep into the muscle and little eddies of blood welled whenever he moved his fingers. Kleiser made no complaints. He didn't even draw Stumm's attention to it, but sat with the wound bared to the warming sun as his injured animals did at the farm where he'd worked in Oestrich-Reingau.

For his part, Stumm ignored him, recognising the wound as superficial despite its bloody appearance. And Scherfe knew better than to comment.

There had also been more intermittent American air-strikes within the perimeter of the German defences. Initially, these had begun with a fury which had caused near panic amongst the laagered panzer commanders, when a squadron of Typhoons had been spotted swooping in from the north. Whilst they were still dots high in the sky the Typhoons had split into three sections, each of four, and the two leading sections had immediately dived into strafing attacks leaving the third section up high on top cover — evidently still wary of the Luftwaffe.

'*Achtung Jabo! Achtung Jabo!*'

Hoarse warnings had rung out above the ceaseless crump of bursting shells and mortar bombs and the panzergrenadiers had turned to the new threat with rising apprehension.

'RAF,' they told each other. 'Is the bloody RAF coming in to give the Yanks a hand?'

But as the leading Typhoons dipped their noses into the attack at upwards of 400 mph they saw that the outer bands of the roundels on the fusilages and beneath the wings were red and not blue. Also, alongside each, the Cross of Lorraine was emblazoned in gold, catching the sun.

Free French!

They knew that the 2nd French Armoured Division was up front with the spearhead of the US 3rd Army, intent only on being first into Paris; but the appearance of French strike-aircraft over the battlefield indicated that French armour must also be close. The net was tightening around the Frundsberg!

Seconds later the grenadiers reeled under the blast of thirty-two rockets, released from the leading section at little above treetop hcight by embittered pilots who had no regard for personal safety. And the rockets exploded diagonally across the German positions like a fast-running fuse, blasting men out of their foxholes and brewing up panzers on the southern perimeter.

The Germans hung on, ignoring their newly wounded, now ready and waiting for the second attacking section. SdKfz 8-ton half-tracks, mounting 2cm multi-barrelled flak guns, had moved out from beneath the trees and were throwing up a barrage of airbursts ahead of the diving Typhoons. At the same time, half-tracks mounting 3·7cm anti-aircraft guns were already engaging the third section on top cover, and black puff-balls of flak were pockmarking the sky around the four aircraft banking in a tight defensive circle.

Grenadier riflemen, with no ammunition to waste taking potshots at fast-moving fighter-bombers, watched from their foxholes as the flak screen thickened. Down slanted another salvo of thirty-two rockets, but the men manning the multi-barrelled flak guns held their range and elevation, blazing into the Typhoons at the precise moment they began to pull from their near vertical strafing dives.

Seconds passed when nothing happened at all. It was only when the Typhoons were beginning to climb that the two trailing aircraft started to stream smoke.

The grenadiers aboard the SdKfzs were too involved to notice, but there was no misinterpreting the ragged cheers of the men who watched one of the Typhoons break up in mid-air and the other begin a crazy spiral which whipped it over the crest of the slope where the American infantry was dug-in. Seconds later, a mushroom of orange flame billowed high above the trees.

There later followed more strafing attacks by USAAF P-47 Thunderbolt fighter-bombers, but these exhibited little of the do-or-die desperation of the Typhoons. The Americans were also wary of causing casualties amongst their own troops to the south, and decided it would be bloody stupid diving into such a pre-ranged concentration of flak anyway. Similar thoughts also occurred to the pilots of heavy bombers which lumbered over the grenadier positions and they turned for home without releasing their loads. Right now, daylight, high-precision bombing was out!

The Germans reinforced their anti-aircraft weapons with a company of SdKfz 10/4s mounting 2cm flak guns which could be used equally effectively against armoured vehicles. These were positioned in and amongst the forward line of Panthers and the PAK screen on the south side of the area skirting the road.

Thus, in a compact all-round defensive circle and with a

channel still open to the rear, the 1st and 2nd Panzergrenadier Battalions settled down to reload belts and magazines and move out more wounded to regimental aid posts.

At 10 am with the battle situation temporarily at stalemate, commanders down to company level were summoned to an Orders Group, for which Brigadefuhrer Dieter Karlsfeld had come forward to assess the opposition still confronting his battle group.

'Nothing has changed!' he told them. 'The Frundsberg Division will cut off the road and seal whatever the Americans have coming east along it!'

Only by slowing down the speed of the enemy advance could the main German forces establish a solid defensive line farther to the east. What the Frundsberg was really doing was buying time!

As Rudi Scherfe joined the line of grenadiers moving to the start-line for the new attack, he looked down ruefully at the maxim cast into the metal of his belt buckle: *UNSERE EHRE HEISST TREUE* – Our Honour is named Loyalty.

There'd been a time – and that not so very long ago – when he'd believed that death in victory was better than life in defeat!

Captain Richard Bannen, commanding No 3 Squadron of the 2nd Regiment of the US 5th Armoured Division, peered through the smoke and shellbursts of the thickening German barrage on to the strip of road which had been a part of their axis of advance.

Since the panzer battalions had withdrawn to their initial start-lines, the American armour had moved up the reverse slope of the hill and were lining the crest almost track to track. This was a haphazard assortment of Shermans which included Calliope tank-busters and Scorpion flame-throwers – a formidable display of strength.

It was apparent to the Americans from the Germans' opening gambit that they'd no idea what they were up against. Just one reconnaissance aircraft would have been sufficient to have put things into perspective for them. Just one, lone Fieseler Storch. But there hadn't been a Kraut airplane sighted during the past three days. Something else! Bannan was content to relax and take his time in knocking hell out of this bunch. SS supermen? What a bloody laugh!

Sergeant Joe Lavanski, commanding No 2 Troop, had similar thoughts running through his mind. But he was also thinking that if No 3 Squadron hadn't been taking its turn in tactical reserve, then he'd have missed out on today's fun. This was the first pitched battle in which the squadron had been involved after three weeks of swanning up and down Normandy chasing the Kraut rearguard.

He'd been bucked up by the division's tactics. That had been pretty smart, pulling back the forward line as soon as the Kraut barrage opened up – even the anti-tank screen – and the Kraut infantry had advanced down the reverse slope and walked like sheep into their Brownings.

But, then, even he had sickened as the squadron's Shermans had rumbled into their new forward location just short of the crest. SS panzergrenadiers or not, it hadn't been all that good crunching a 40-ton tank over dead and wounded human beings, squashing the poor bastards like beetles, so that their blood and guts squirted as high as the turret and their entrails got snatched up by the driving sprocket and festooned the tracks. He was glad the engine had drowned the crunch of their bones. But none of this had been the squadron's fault. The Krauts should have heaped their casualties on to the panzers as well as their walking wounded!

The box barrage had also been a helluva success! Pinned the SS back on their start-line as effectively as a fifty-foot, bomb-proof wall! The Frog Typhoons hadn't had things all their own way, though, but they'd have their chance later on. That was for sure! This was going to be curtains for one more SS regiment. What was the fancy name these buggers called themselves? Frundsberg? The bastards were going to regret ever leaving Russia!

The German second barrage was misdirected from the start. Pitched on to the original American positions in sparse woodland beyond the reverse slopes, the gunner officers had neither Intelligence nor reconnaissance reports to indicate that the enemy had moved forward after their initial probing counterattack.

Even so, considering German artillery problems during this phase of the Battle of Normandy, the barrage had both depth and concentration. Fire-control was masterly. More medium batteries had joined the Frundsberg SPs and the hollow whirr-whirr of the shells over the waiting panzergrenadiers gave them new confidence. Reinforcement mortar teams had also come forward from Divisional Reserve and were bracketing the reverse slope with 81mm high-explosive bombs, the grenadiers keeping as many as fifteen bombs in the air from each of the giant mortars.

The PAK anti-tank screen, in front of the grenadier battalions, divided to the flanks and the Panthers moved through the
gap with the grenadiers aboard. There was a new urgency
about this second attack, more aggression in the savage roar of
the panzers' exhausts and the steady thump-thump-thump of
their 75mm guns as they boosted the SP barrage on trajectory.
Also up front with the panzers were SdKfz 10/4 half-tracks,
seeking out the forward line of American armour.

Sturmann Klaus Stumm and his MG-42 section hung on to
the pitching turret of a flank Panther. They were keyed up for
the attack, Stumm with the machine gun clutched to his chest
and the loose end of the ammunition belt flapping with the
rolling of the panzer. Kleiser, heedless of his wound, caught
the flaying end as Stumm jerked a round into the breech.

Kleiser was beginning to bleed copiously after the exertion
of the attack, blood streaming from his fingertips, soaking his
tunic and forming into rivulets which coursed down the grey
steel of the panzer turret. He had swapped his Schmeiser
machine pistol for a panzerfaust infantry anti-tank projector,
which he had salvaged from amongst the dead during the withdrawal. He had only one hollow-charge bomb and this was
clamped in the weapon. There was a dogged expression on the
big man's face which said that he'd already taken enough
hammer from the Yanks that morning and didn't mean to take
any more!

It also struck Scherfe that Kleiser no longer looked such a
country clod. Even the too-small helmet with the usual strands
of reddish hair protruding beneath it appeared normal. Scherfe
couldn't guess how or why Kleiser had suddenly turned
himself into the kind of soldier who can shrug off a serious
wound and still be eager for more battle. He knew that he felt
like an Aunt Sally on one of the stalls at the village fairs he used
to visit with his mother when he was a kid. If the Yanks missed
knocking him over the first time, then round he'd come again
and again until, eventually, he was toppled! That was what this
kind of mad frontal attack amounted to. The general brief – to
hold back American reinforcements to give a breathing space
to units back east – was just so much balls!

There *was* no main defence line. All there was to the east
was the Dives river, when they'd expected to get as far as the
Sarthe, and it was his bet that the soldiers lucky enough to be
close were scrambling across every bridge and every ford they
found passable.

Now they'd been briefed that the battalion's prime objective was no longer only the road in front of them and its dominating slopes to the south, but also three villages beyond the reverse slope! The young untersturmfuhrer who'd given them that information had insisted there was no point in sealing off a main axis if the enemy could open up a secondary route round the back. That made sense, but it was asking a hell of a lot from a grenadier battalion already depleted after one rout that morning.

Beyond the road, the Panthers with their sections of grenadiers aboard deployed into line-abreast formation, the supporting companies giving depth to the attack.

There came no reply from the Americans, though the German barrage maintained its initial intensity and was scheduled to creep forward to the enemy support lines once the first line of panzers had topped the crest.

But still nothing happened. Even the American medium batteries, way back, were silent.

Worried panzer commanders spoke urgently to their own commanders, seeking a change of orders. If the Yanks were letting them top the rise without engaging, then it was a certainty they'd got something ready and waiting for them down the reverse slope!

By this time, the Panther formation was rumbling up the steeper slopes in low gear, pouring smoke from exhausts already glowing red with overheating. The grenadiers were looking strained, poised to dive for ground cover at the first sign of American armour or anti-tank guns.

But it was not Shermans which hit the panzers first, but a couple of squadrons of P-47 Thunderbolt fighter-bombers which topped the crest seconds before they did. This was a tactical manoeuvre timed to the last split-second. Two-hundred-and-fifty pound high-explosive bombs blasted amongst the now-struggling panzers at a time and place where there was no natural cover and the grenadiers were unprotected.

The second wave of Thunderbolts duplicated the first run and within seconds the slope became littered with burning and crippled Panthers. Crews and the grenadiers were shredded into bone, sinew and blood before they could get clear. Others, who had been able to dash a few metres away, were doused in high octane petrol, more searing than napalm, and ran screaming through the exploding bombs with their uniforms on fire, careering in demented circles until they collapsed into charred heaps.

At the precise moment the last of the US fighter-bombers cleared the battle ground, there came the concerted roar of tank engines from beyond the crest. Panzergrenadier officers winced, feverishly pulling out Kampfpistoles and shooting off violet flares. The extent of their commitment was there for all to see. Not only had the forward panzer battalions been caught in the open by the USAAF, but they'd also moved blindly into an armoured trap.

Immediately the German barrage shortened its range, desperately attempting to cripple the Shermans before they could inject momentum into their attack. But the gunners were too late. The leading US tanks were already climbing up through their gears, 81mm tank-busting guns loaded and steady. Then they were speeding down the slope on to panzers still reeling from the ferocity of the air-strike.

At the sight of the first line of Shermans the grenadiers leapt to the ground, huddling behind the Panthers, seeking protection from the heavy calibre American guns and the Browning crossfire. Still forward, Klaus Stumm and his MG-42 section hung on to the attack, Stumm happier where he could strike at the American infantry. It was the support companies who'd have to face grenades and mortars as well as carpet-shelling. If a man kept close to the enemy infantry he could be safe from all that.

The Americans began sending smoke shells over the German positions to the rear, screening the forward slopes from supporting weapons. But still the panzergrenadiers pushed on with small groups moving ahead of the panzers; men with their Schmeisers hanging from their necks creeping up to the battened-down Shermans, to clamp sticky grenades to the vulnerable armour at the turret-swivel.

Soon Shermans also began to burn and, as they exploded, so the grenadiers reformed into a concerted attack and stormed up the hill with no American infantry yet in sight. The PAK anti-tank screen had taken up positions on the flanks heedless of the lack of cover, the gunners slamming armour-piercing shells into the breeches of their 75s and firing over open sights into the massing Shermans.

Troop Sergeant Joe Lavanski knew that the 3rd Squadron was taking most of the hammering. Being in the vanguard of an armoured strike didn't have all the glory he'd thought it would. Their problem, right now, was that supporting infantry wasn't being committed. They were still somewhere south over the rise, massed along the northern perimeter of the wood waiting to mow down the Kraut infantry as they topped the crest. That was great! But until they moved the Shermans were at the mercy of the bastards!

Besides, no tankman liked being battened down when enemy infantry was around. For one thing they couldn't see a damn thing through their periscopes closer than fifteen feet and the Krauts had perfected their sniping at the slits. The floor of the tank was already thick with shattered periscopes! This was like playing blind man's buff with high-explosive! The bastards were simply strolling up to the Shermans and picking their spots to clamp their goddamn sticky grenades — on the turret-swivel or the driving sprocket. They appeared to like the sprocket best and stood around watching the track snake off. Then they got down to their Schmeisers and Spandaus and waited for the tank crew to climb out.

Shermans were too bloody vulnerable without infantry support and the smouldering pyres which littered the hillside proved as much. It was traumatic inside a battened-down tank, even without the Krauts pitching high-explosive at you. The scream of the great engine, the thud of the gun and a kind of airless temperature which set the oil and cordite fumes solid in a man's lungs. It was like trying to breathe in a coffin which had steel sides eight inches thick. Then, without warning, they'd become a crematorium, so hot that the armour plate glowed red. But the difference about this crematorium was that the bodies which had got trapped there were still alive. For a coupla minutes, anyhow!

Christ!

Lavanski wished he'd not been so keen to rejoin the main body of the regiment. Reconnaissance had its problems, but it was a helluva cleaner life than this!

He had set his eyes closer to the periscope, looking out on to the gyrating tank battle in front of him. Some German PAK-75s were brazenly pitched in the open and blasting away at the Shermans with armour-piercing shells. At times like this a man could forget he was looking through a periscope and duck his head on reflex as streams of tracer slashed straight for his eyes.

He called down to his driver, voice barely audible above the noise of battle, even over the intercom.

'Keep to the spaces, Vince! To the left o' the burning crates!'

'Sure, Skip . . .'

The Sherman bucked as Vince Egan boosted the throttle and quickened the right hand track. But, as he straightened up, a panzergrenadier suddenly appeared in the Sherman's path.

He was an enormous man with his helmet perched incongruously on top of his great head and clumps of reddish hair sticking out from beneath it. His left arm appeared to have been shattered and the uniform sleeve was running with blood. But as Lavanski watched, the grenadier unhurriedly raised a panzerfaust anti-tank projector to his shoulder and took deliberate aim as though he'd all the time in the world.

Lavanski found his voice, yelling to his gunner.

'Chop that big bastard, Leo! Quick! for Christ's sake ...!'

And those were the last words which Sergeant Joe Lavanski of Cleveland, Ohio, ever spoke, for before Leo Dilman could align his Browning, Helmut Kleiser had squeezed the trigger of his panzerfaust and the bomb sped straight as an arrow to clout the Sherman bang on the turret-swivel.

Kleiser waited until the Sherman erupted in a sudden surge of orange flame. Then he hurled the panzerfaust at the burning tank and grinned down at Klaus Stumm with an expression that said, 'Follow that, you clever bastard!'

As the American armour slowly but surely ground to a halt, there came a new bombardment behind which the Shermans began a systematic withdrawal. Panzer commanders, anticipating this, pushed closer to the Shermans to avoid the shelling. In consequence it was the grenadiers who caught most of the barrage. High-explosive and napalm shells tore into the unprotected platoons. Hastily dug positions were obliterated and the whole front of Frundsberg grenadiers was shattered under a weight of shelling they'd never experienced before.

But, five minutes later, the barrage lifted to the German support lines, leaving the hillside thick with the dead and screaming wounded. Then came the second Sherman attack, undeterred, the reverse slopes crawling with line after line of newly committed tanks, the forward squadrons machine-gunning and flaming everything that moved.

Behind the tanks came the American infantry, moving quickly to keep pace with the Shermans, looking highly-operational, fit and eager for the fight.

Scared that their offensive could be on the point of bogging down, Frundsberg commanders transmitted orders direct to Panther and grenadier commanders to the effect that the strip of road had to be held at all costs until the 275th Infantry Division arrived on the scene.

The troops reacted at once and small groups of survivors from the shelling, the flamings and the machine gunning, reassembled and once again stormed forward in a hopeless counterattack, seeking paths through the Shermans to get at the American infantry.

More violet flares soared and once again down came the German barrage, sufficiently finely ranged to envelop the American support waves. The remaining Panthers again moved forward with grenadiers leaping from cover to scramble aboard, their warcries ringing above the pandemonium of the shelling. On sped the Panthers, bludgeoning their way through the American anti-tank screen, rolling and bucking over the undulating ground and firing with an intensity which pinned the Americans back into defence.

The Americans shook themselves and called up more reserves, which again advanced in waves. Unfaltering, straight lines of Shermans staggered deep with their 75mm guns spitting out armour-piercing shells as fast as the gunners could load.

Slowly, the German attack began to lose its momentum as the few remaining Panthers were brewed up. Others, with tracks broken, were being manned as strongpoints and isolated battles began to develop in which grenadiers, vicious as cornered rats, turned on the advancing Shermans with hollow-charge grenades and swept the support infantry with machine gun fire.

In the second American wave, Lieutenant Roger Bailey had positioned his Platoon Headquarters Group between his No 2 and No 3 Sections, all in extended line.

'Don't bunch, goddamn it! For Christ's sake spread out and look to your front!'

Anxiety had lifted the pitch of his voice so that it sounded churlish even in the heat of battle. But the soldiers on the flank moved wider, giving those in the centre more room. It stood to reason that if they bunched then one shell or a single burst of machine gun fire could knock a dozen over at the same time. Even so, bunched or not, it was the closeness of a friend which gave most of them the courage to keep moving on into the holocaust.

Bailey didn't feel any more adequate now than he had two days earlier when his platoon had blundered into the Kraut machine gun post on the hill top. There he'd lost four men and they'd found one panzergrenadier on the objective with half his head blown away – with his own Luger, Bailey had decided. The rest of the bastards had flown! That wasn't good. By Christ, it wasn't good at all!

To his left was Vic Sullivan's No 1 Section, thin on the

ground, but still operational. To his right was Standish's section and, beyond them, Minzetti's. So far they'd had no casualties, but there'd been some fierce blasts too close for comfort. What Bailey didn't like was the number of one-man flame-thrower kits which had been distributed amongst his platoon immediately prior to the attack, and he tried not to look at Private Rix Dimmans a couple of yards to his right. Dimmans was a small man and the wide, circular, cylindrical napalm container strapped to his back liked a great automobile tyre dwarfed him. Neither did the man himself look too happy, as he clutched the flame gun with both hands, his rifle slung over a shoulder, constantly slipping and causing him to stumble.

Bailey knew that everybody hated these goddamn flame-thrower packs. Sure, they got warm enough to burn up a panzer which had been careless enough to leave a hatch open. And they could root out infantry from foxholes and cellars quicker than any HE bomb. But they were a helluva thing to lug around and were also top of the list for Kraut snipers – even rating above officers and signallers carrying R/T sets! Germans didn't like being fried alive either!

But the real crunch came when the guy carrying the pack got himself hit – invariably with an incendiary bullet – and then the container and its wearer erupted in a searing fireball which shrivelled him into a blackened skeleton in seconds, and at the same time showered men within a ten yards radius with flaming napalm.

So Bailey was keeping a wary eye on Private Rix Dimmans and wishing to hell the guy was marching some place else!

In a hollow which they had scooped out for themselves along the forward edge of a small copse, Stumm and his section were dug in with the MG-42. Though the strike wave of American infantry had wilted under the weight and accuracy of their fire, more Shermans and more infantry were getting dangerously close. But they were taking their time about it – and that could be worrying! It was as though the Yanks were telling them they didn't plan to chop them up until they were good and ready!

Besides, there was more activity over to the left flank, from where it looked as though a diversionary attack might spring at any time. To the rear, giant B-29 Flying Fortresses, C47 Douglas Dakotas and fighter-bombers were strafing and pattern-bombing. Grenadier commanders, committed on the slopes, had little time to think up tactical reasons for this and assumed that Divisional Headquarters was getting a priority bombardment.

Stumm crouched behind the MG-42 machine gun with a full belt threaded, waiting for the PAK-75 gunners and the few Panthers still operational to contain the leading Shermans.

At his side, Scherfe and Kleiser lay belly-flat with their Schmeisers on the ground in front of them. Ammunition was dangerously low and supplies were no longer coming forward. Stumm would use what was left of the 7·92mm Spandau ammunition at medium range and then they'd take up the action with Schmeisers. After that, they'd rely on the rifles which Scherfe and Kleiser had lugged across Normandy on the off-chance of just such a crisis.

So much of the artillery support had dwindled, as casualties amongst self-propelled guns and gunners had risen under American heavy bomber sorties, that they were no longer able to maintain co-ordinated fire plans. As it was, the few pieces still firing were switching from flank to flank to spread out what effective support they could manage.

Grim though the outlook was, Frundsberg commanders were acutely aware that if the division were to survive this battle, then they had to maintain their depleted forces on the offensive, resorting to bombs and grenades if their artillery support eventually petered out.

So back into the attack came the battered Panthers and, as they blazed into the American armour, more Shermans brewed-up and others slewed round impotently on broken tracks. Small groups of grenadiers stormed in and amongst them with sticky bombs and panzerschreck projectors, whilst the PAK-75s fired off their few remaining armour-piercing shells into a scattering of disabled Shermans which had set themselves up as armoured strongpoints.

At this point the American diversionary assault which had been threatening from the left flank materialised with a crash of artillery and a saturation of exploding shells. Lines of Shermans emerged from cover whilst the infantry remained amongst the bushes and trees and enfiladed withering fire on to the grenadiers facing the main frontal attack. But groups of them broke clear and raced to the flank, where a number of isolated battles sprang up along the perimeter of the wood. These were machine gun to machine gun, man to man . . . but then a second wave of American armour broke through them with a centre core of armoured personnel carriers fitted with

149

rocket launchers and transporting special commando groups of US Rangers.

Immediately the small battles fizzled into nothing as the new force struck savagely at the main German positions astride the crest of the hill. A few PAKs swung on traverse to meet the infantry, which was doubling forward bravely under the concentrated fire of grenadiers' machine guns.

Amongst the first wave of infantry, Lieutenant Roger Bailey and his platoon surged forward with the attack, breathing hard after their long advance up the slope. Now, with the spirited support coming in from the flank, much of Bailey's initial foreboding had left him, for he could see by the number of burning panzers and German dead littering the battlefield that the end of German resistance must surely be in sight.

The platoon advanced steadily, holding its position in the long line of American infantry, the soldiers with their bayonets fixed, tommy-guns held firmly at the hip, safety catches forward; the four flame-thrower operators positioned towards the middle of the sections, some of them as wary of their new piece of equipment as they were of the entrenched panzergrenadiers.

'All right, you guys! Let's quicken it up!' Bailey yelled.

The problem was that no way could he estimate the strength of the opposition. The grenadiers had gone to ground as their leading panzers had brewed-up and the bastards were holding their fire, waiting for them to get close.

Klaus Stumm, unperturbed by the sudden fury of the flank attack, crouched behind the MG-42 machine gun as relaxed as ever. Four ammunition belts had been clipped together and Scherfe had folded them meticulously at the right side of the gun. Now he lay next to Stumm with his hands hovering over the belts, ready to feed them into the breech as Stumm opened fire.

To Stumm's left, Kleiser had primed his three remaining stick grenades. He grinned sourly to himself as he watched the American infantry doubling towards them.

Stumm tightened his forefinger about the trigger, eyes slitted as he peered through thinning smoke from the burning Shermans, calculating the range. Maybe there was a full company of them, but with the first burst he could knock out most of the centre platoon. They were bloody stupid coming at them in a frontal like that when they'd got so much armour in support.

The range shrank to a hundred metres . . . seventy-five . . . fifty. Stumm squeezed the trigger and the Spandau responded

with its immediate, impatient prrt-prrt-prrt. And as Scherfe
scooped away the empty cartridge cases from beneath the gun,
so Roger Bailey's platoon began to die. Few of them stumbled
or were even thrown back by the accurate cone of fire. None of
them screamed. They just fell forward on to their knees and
remained in that position, whilst those who still ran looked
about them, anxious, vulnerable.

Bailey shook himself, preparing to dive for cover, but when
he glanced along the line of the advance he saw that little of the
momentum had been lost, despite the machine guns. He
swallowed hard against a bitter taste of fear, still shouting
encouragement.

'Keep going, fellers! Keep going!'

And he quickened his pace so that he was yards ahead of
most of his men, a Colt automatic clutched in his hand.

'Come on for Chrissake! We gotta run at the bastards!'

He saw then that the platoon had lost about half its strength
but, for some reason he couln't explain, the Kraut machine gun
had also ceased firing. Even as he closed the distance he found
his brain demanding to know the reason why. They were
almost upon the spot where he'd seen the first muzzle flashes.
Were the Krauts just hanging on? Hanging on to make their
killing all the more positive?

But in the copse, Stumm and Scherfe were working frantically on the MG-42.

'Bloody stoppage!'

Stumm snarled the words as he worked the cocking handle,
clearing the breech. Scherfe had switched barrels. Stumm
jerked another round into the chamber. Scherfe held the
ammunition belt steady and level. Stumm took aim, preparing
to traverse. He was running out of time, the Yanks were less
than thirty metres away and coming hard. He squeezed the
trigger. Crack! A single shot and the gun seized again. Christ!
He glared at Scherfe. This was no simple stoppage. Could be
that the piston had seized! Bloody hopeless!

He toppled the gun from his shoulder and grabbed Kleiser's
discarded Schmeiser.

Bailey's teeth bared in a wild, elated grin. The clever
bastards had clogged their gun! He was grinning as he turned
to little Rix Dimmans, who was managing to keep pace with
the attack despite the flame-thrower harnessed to his back.
Bailey took a couple of steps towards him as he ran, pointing to
the line of trees where he'd last seen the Spandau muzzle flash.

'Burn the bastards, Rix! Now! Burn 'em!'

Dimmans didn't hesitate. He squeezed the trigger of the flame-gun and an electric spark jumped the points as pressurised napalm squirted from the nozzle and a sudden, piercing tongue of flame hosed into the copse. But Dimmans' aim was high and the foliage high in the trees flared in the heat. He dropped the nozzle, trying to see through the smoke he'd made.

But as he levelled the flame-gun for a second burst, Helmut Kleiser charged from cover with a stick grenade in each hand. Bailey saw him coming — a giant figure storming at the platoon through the smoke — and he blazed away wildly with his Colt, firing half a dozen shots and missing with five. But Kleiser didn't flinch, sensing the ·45-inch bullets zipping past his body, and he took his time in hurling the stick grenades into the front line of American infantry which had begun to sprint the last twenty metres to the grenadier positions. He snatched the third grenade from his belt and threw it as Bailey's sixth shot struck him in the hip. He spun to the ground as the first of his grenades exploded at the running feet of Private Rix Dimmans. He saw the fireball from the flame-thrower suddenly envelop the small man and a shower of flaming napalm deluge ten or fifteen others.

By this time Stumm and Scherfe had their Schmeisers at their shoulders, holding fire for fear of hitting Kleiser; but, as he fell, so they opened up in unison and their fusilade toppled over most of the survivors of Kleiser's brave attack.

As the fireball died Scherfe threw down his Schmeiser intent on looking to Kleiser, but Stumm seized his arm in a vice grip and when Scherfe spun round to him, angry, he saw none of the wildness in the sturmann's eyes he'd expected to be there.

'Let's go!' Stumm said. And he heaved Scherfe bodily towards the trees.

But Scherfe stood his ground, shaking his head. Kleiser had saved their lives for the second time that morning. First with the Sherman. Now with the flame-thrower. But for Kleiser they'd both be dead. They couldn't desert the man now!

Stumm knew what was going through the boy's mind and, for once, he explained. 'He'll be all right! The Yanks don't kill their prisoners. They'll see he's all right!'

He pointed through the still-billowing smoke from the flame-thrower and beyond the piles of dead surrounding it to where a second wave of American infantry was topping the crest. To the flanks Scherfe saw that other groups of grenadiers were pulling back and it was this which caused him to follow

Stumm. In that instant, the truth had hammered into his brain.

The 10th SS Panzer Division Frundsberg had broken!

Christ! But that wasn't possible, was it? The Frundsberg running? But there were grenadiers streaming from their positions with American personnel carriers and their complements of US Rangers hard on their heels, the withering firepower from each carrier blasting shards of scything steel amongst them.

He sought Stumm's face as they stumbled through the bracken, seeking the cover of the denser parts of the wood where neither Shermans nor US Rangers could get at them.

Impossible or not, Frundsberg had broken!

It was midday by the time Stumm and Scherfe, as ever moving eastwards, cleared what had been the 10th SS Panzer Division Frundsberg's operational area, but there was an uncertainty about their plans. For now they knew what had been the American heavy bombers' and fighter-bombers' priority targets over the past three days and that these were only remotely connected with the slowing down of German supplies to forward units.

They were keeping to the high ground parallel to the main Argentan-Exmes road because the valley was choked with the dead and the devastated equipment of two German armies. Stumm, reacting to the portent of such defeat and annihilation as acutely as Scherfe, strode forcefully across the high meadows with Kleiser's rifle slung over his shoulder, eyes roaming the distant horizon beyond which ran the Dives river.

It was evident to Scherfe that Stumm had, at last, reached his breaking point. At long last he'd had enough of war, but he hadn't suddenly degenerated into a shrieking, screaming imbecile as Scherfe had believed he would. He'd shrunk into himself in a kind of introspection which spelled disillusionment. Had Kreutzmann lived, maybe he'd have tipped beyond the rim of sanity, Scherfe thought. Maybe if Kleiser hadn't suddenly found he could be a hero . . .

They hadn't exchanged a word during the past two hours. That was because they had handkerchieves over their mouths and nostrils to lessen the sickening stench of death and putrefaction which drifted up in invisible clouds from the lower ground where the roads, the sparsely wooded foothills, meadows, farmsteads and irrigation ditches were piled with the bodies of uninterred German soldiers and their animals.

This was what had happened to the main force of the mighty German 5th and 7th Armies!

This was the kind of havoc the Americans had wrought with their heavy bombers and artillery. The most awesome thing about it was the demoralising unholy silence which hung over the endlees heaps of mutilated, rotting flesh.

They came upon what remained of a road convoy, the trucks neatly tipped over into an irrigation ditch, all at the same side of the road, caught by a single stick of HE bombs. And the blackened, naked things strewn about the verges were German bodies which had spilled out of the trucks.

But, as they came closer still, they saw there were red crosses painted on the grey canvas covers and that these were not trucks at all, but ambulances. Scherfe's mind flew to the wounded who'd been sent back east from Thielker's detachment and his body chilled. Was this as far as the poor devils had got before the USSAF caught up with them? He could see now that many of the mutilated, bloated bodies were not wearing helmets. He could even pick out the colour of their hair. Long hair! Women's hair! Nurses! German nurses! Some depraved bastard had sacrificed a hospital column to get at the SS!

But Scherfe, like Stumm, could do no more than shrug his own impotence as he hurried past. It was too late, now. Everything was too late now!

They came upon the bomb-shattered gun emplacements of a medium artillery battery, the long barrels pointing skywards in all directions, heaps of brass shellcases scattered around and amongst the dead gunners, catching the sun. There were also dead draught horses, their stomachs distended to gigantic proportions.

In the foothills lay what remained of an infantry patrol caught by an American air bombardment. For over a couple of hundred metres the trees had been blasted bare and were festooned with fragments of human bodies, strips of field-grey uniform and strands of leather equipment. On the ground lay their weapons: mortars, infantry anti-tank projectors, MG-42 machine guns and rifles. Weapons of death with only dead hands to work them.

They climbed into the hills, higher above the stinking roadside ditches each with its filling of dead; men who'd been rooted out from cover by napalm, strawberry red beside the blackened corpes of their comrades who'd died under the cleaner blast of high-explosive.

Closer to the river the dead lay thicker and the roads

became solid with vehicles. Mk VI Tiger panzers stood nose-to-tail with supply trucks, all of them blackened by fire. More dead! Everywhere bodies rotting and fouling the air with their putrefaction.

Neither Stumm nor Scherfe paid any attention to the lone Westland Lysander which buzzed in systematic runs up and down the line of the road. One thing was for certain. It wasn't range-spotting for the US artillery any more! Probably taking pattern-photographs as positive proof that General George Patten wasn't shooting off his mouth and that two German armies really had been devastated in this lush farmland west of the Dives river. Or perhaps some lesser known Yank General was looking over the results of his desk-planning in person?

Who cared, anyway?

They didn't even hear the rising note of the Lysander's single engine or notice that the aircraft had banked in their direction. The first indication that either the pilot or his passenger had decided upon a little private hunting was the rattle of Vickers machine guns and the clip-clip-clip of bullets scything through the trees above them. They dived for cover, cursing the man. Hadn't there been enough killing here in this valley without the bastard seeking more scalps? What harm could two survivors from a decimated SS division do to the great American war machine when the entire campaign was lost?

Scherfe pushed himself up from the ground as the Lysander lifted its nose from the leisurely, glide-in attack and stalked angrily to the centre of the woodland track. There he halted, waiting for Stumm.

'Sturmann!' he called. 'Sturmann?'

Scherfe hurried to the place where he'd seen Stumm go to ground and he found him lying in a patch of gorse, flat on his back and with his eyes open to the sky. His arms were stretched straight down his sides as though he had been standing to attention and had just toppled over.

Scherfe stared down at him, conscious of the breeze stirring the man's curling blond hair; looking into the pale blue eyes which had miraculously lost all their venom and were already beginning to glaze.

Scherfe shook his head in disbelief. Klaus Stumm wasn't dead. That just couldn't be, dear God. That was just bloody silly. Stumm could never die! And he continued to stare at the still body as though life might have returned to it during that brief moment of introspection.

He saw, then, that there was a patch of bright, red blood

beginning to darken the tunic in a widening circle right of the second button, highlighting the small dark hole where the bullet had gone through to the heart.

He dropped his Schmeiser into the gorse and scooped off his helmet and tossed it on top of the gun. If Sturmann Stumm were dead, then why wasn't he cheering his head off? Why was he looking down at Stumm's body as though he'd lost a friend? Why was he watching his hair flick in the wind? Why, for Christ's sake, didn't he just go?

He reached out a hand and closed Stumm's eyes as he'd seen old folk do back home and was surprised to find the lids still warm. But at the contact he pulled himself upright, quickly, as though he had been burned. He wasn't getting sentimental about Klaus Stumm, was he? He jerked out a harsh laugh at such incongruity. Sentimental about Klaus Stumm? A real laugh that – getting sentimental about Sturmann Stumm!

Hadn't Stumm been an out-and-out bastard for as long as he'd known him? Worse! All that time he'd been bordering on insanity! A crazy, homicidal, fighting animal who'd lived only for the kicks he got from killing, rape, mutilation and torture. Had there been no war, he'd have spent most of his life behind bars in some high-security mental institution. Besides, he'd been callously egocentric; cruelly indifferent to the sufferings of others; too ready to sacrifice lives to preserve his own!

An out-and-out bastard. But, yet . . . but, yet . . .

But yet, by Christ, the man had been a soldier! If the rest of the Wehrmacht had shown a glimmer of the sturmann's dedication to his Fuhrer, then the German 5th and 7th Armies wouldn't be sprawling dead in the valleys west of the Dives river!

Scherfe unclipped the empty Schmeiser magazine pouches from his belt, unbuckled his leather equipment and tossed the lot on top of his helmet and machine pistol. He turned to go, shoving his hands deep into his trouser pockets, tunic open at the neck. He was no longer a soldier! Whatever the Wehrmacht planned to do next they could do it without him!

But then, as a new thought struck him, he turned back on impulse to Stumm's body and unfastened the two breast pockets of the tunic, exploring inside with thumb and forefinger of each hand at the same time. He produced a couple of cigarette ends, tinder-dry and stained brown; a single five-mark piece and a pack of chewing gum with an American label. That was all! Scherfe looked down at them and then threw them into the undergrowth.

What had he been expecting to find? A dog-eared photograph of a pretty German girl with a baby on her lap, a picture of a grey-haired old lady, smiling and waving from the door of a rose-covered cottage?

Jesus! This was no ordinary soldier! This was Klaus Stumm, who'd have slit the girl's throat rather than marry her. Besides, he'd never had a mother! Stumm was conceived in a 75mm shellcase!

Scherfe looked up at the sky and the midday sun which slanted brightly through the trees to dapple the ground at his feet. Then he wandered off in the direction he guessed was east.

NEL BESTSELLERS

T037061	BLOOD AND MONEY	*Thomas Thompson*	£1.50
T045692	THE BLACK HOLE	*Alan Dean Foster*	95p
T049817	MEMORIES OF ANOTHER DAY	*Harold Robbins*	£1.95
T049701	THE DARK	*James Herbert*	£1.50
T045528	THE STAND	*Stephen King*	£1.75
T065475	I BOUGHT A MOUNTAIN	*Thomas Firbank*	£1.50
T050203	IN THE TEETH OF THE EVIDENCE	*Dorothy L. Sayers*	£1.25
T050777	STRANGER IN A STRANGE LAND	*Robert Heinlein*	£1.75
T050807	79 PARK AVENUE	*Harold Robbins*	£1.75
T042308	DUNE	*Frank Herbert*	£1.50
T045137	THE MOON IS A HARSH MISTRESS	*Robert Heinlein*	£1.25
T050149	THE INHERITORS	*Harold Robbins*	£1.75
T049620	RICH MAN, POOR MAN	*Irwin Shaw*	£1.60
T046710	EDGE 36: TOWN ON TRIAL	*George G. Gilman*	£1.00
T037541	DEVIL'S GUARD	*Robert Elford*	£1.25
T050629	THE RATS	*James Herbert*	£1.25
T050874	CARRIE	*Stephen King*	£1.50
T050610	THE FOG	*James Herbert*	£1.25
T041867	THE MIXED BLESSING	*Helen Van Slyke*	£1.50
T038629	THIN AIR	*Simpson & Burger*	95p
T038602	THE APOCALYPSE	*Jeffrey Konvitz*	95p
T046850	WEB OF EVERYWHERE	*John Brunner*	85p

NEL P.O. BOX 11, FALMOUTH TR10 9EN, CORNWALL

Postage charge:

U.K. Customers. Please allow 40p for the first book, 18p for the second book, 13p for each additional book ordered, to a maximum charge of £1.49, in addition to cover price.

B.F.P.O. & Eire. Please allow 40p for the first book, 18p for the second book, 13p per copy for the next 7 books, thereafter 7p per book, in addition to cover price.

Overseas Customers. Please allow 60p for the first book plus 18p per copy for each additional book, in addition to cover price.

Please send cheque or postal order (no currency).

Name ....

Address ....

....

Title ....

While every effort is made to keep prices steady, it is sometimes necessary to increase prices at short notice. New English Library reserve the right to show on covers and charge new retail prices which may differ from those advertised in the text or elsewhere.(5)